EVERYMAN'S CLASSIC PUZZLES

Everyman's Classic Puzzles

GYLES BRANDRETH

GUILD PUBLISHING
LONDON

This edition published 1985 by
Book Club Associates

by arrangement with
J. M. Dent & Sons Ltd
Aldine House, 33 Welbeck Street, London W1M 8LX

British Library Cataloguing in Publication Data

Brandreth, Gyles
  Everyman's classic puzzles.
  1. Classic puzzles
  1. Title
  793.73   GV1493

  ISBN 0-460-04676-4

CONTENTS

INTRODUCTION

It seems that mankind has always enjoyed puzzles. In the earliest recorded literature, in scripture and in legend, we find riddles, enigmas and conundrums. It seems that as soon as man invented language he invented word puzzles. Mathematical puzzles, too, are as old as mathematics itself. Indeed some branches of mathematics – topology and probability theory are two modern examples – originated from the study of puzzles.

This book opens with a selection of puzzles from ancient Greece and it concludes with three programs to enable computers to generate brand-new puzzles – from the cradle of civilization to tomorrow's technology! – taking as its scope the best of every type of puzzle of past, present and future.

In this book you will find puzzles from old Arabic and Hindu sources, puzzles devised by medieval scholars, puzzles from such eminent Victorians as Lewis Carroll. You will find many traditional puzzles that have been passed on from generation to generation. You will find puzzles composed by a British prime minister and a British monarch. You will find the best creations of the greatest names in puzzledom – people such as Sam Loyd, H. E. Dudeney, Afrit, Torquemada, Ximenes, Hubert Phillips, Martin Gardner. Although the sources of most of the puzzles are English and American, the world of puzzledom is international, and you will also find puzzles translated from other languages such as French and Russian.

Whatever your taste in puzzles, you will find in this book a wealth of interest. There are word puzzles, number puzzles, logic puzzles, chess puzzles, visual puzzles, puzzles with coins, with matches, with dominoes, and much, much more besides.

All the puzzles have star ratings to indicate level of difficulty. Such gradings can only be subjective and approximate, but they are often found to be helpful. Here is what they indicate:

☆ Very easy
☆☆ Easy
☆☆☆ Average
☆☆☆☆ Difficult
☆☆☆☆☆ Fiendish

The most comprehensive puzzle collection ever assembled lies in wait for you. Enjoy it!

Gyles Brandreth

$\frac{1}{2} + \frac{1}{8} + \frac{1}{13} + \frac{1}{20}$

$\frac{4}{40} \quad \frac{1}{10}$

$\begin{matrix} 6 & 4 \\ 7 & 3 \end{matrix}$

$\begin{matrix} x2-1 & =-1 \\ 4 & 8 \end{matrix}$

1. OLD MASTERS

THE ANCIENT GREEKS

The ancient Greeks took mathematics quite seriously. The names of
Euclid and Pythagoras, for example, are familiar to every scholar. But
when they were not busy dropping perpendiculars and constructing
squares on hypotenuses, they could relax with an entertaining puzzle,
like the five that follow.

1. The Statue of Pallas ☆☆

The following inscription was on a statue of Pallas Athene: 'I, Pallas, am
made of beaten gold, the gift of the poets. Half was given by Kariseus, an
eighth by Thespis; Solon gave a tenth, and Themison a twentieth. The
remaining nine talents were the gift of Aristodicus.'

How many talents of gold were there in the statue?

2. The Mule and the Donkey ☆

According to legend, Euclid was the author of this puzzle. 'A mule and a
donkey were carrying a load of sacks. The donkey groaned, so the mule
said to him: "Why are you complaining? If you gave me one sack, I
would have twice as many as you; and if I gave you one of my sacks, then
we would have equal loads." '

How many sacks was each carrying?

3. The House of Pythagoras ☆☆

Polykrates the money-lender said to Pythagoras: 'Blessed Pythagoras,
scion of the Muses, answer my question. How many scholars dwell in
your house?'

Pythagoras replied: 'I will tell thee, Polykrates. Half of the scholars
are dedicated to literature; a quarter apply themselves to the study of the
wonders of nature; and one-seventh contemplate in silence. There are
also three women, of whom the greatest is Theano. That is the number of
scholars beneath my roof.'

How many scholars were in the house of Pythagoras?

4. **The Graces and the Muses** ☆

The three Graces were carrying baskets of apples, in each basket the same number of apples. They met the nine Muses, and gave them each the same number of apples, and so the nine Muses and the three Graces had each the same number.

How many apples were in each basket?

5. **Demochares** ☆

Demochares has lived one-fourth of his life as a boy, one-fifth as a youth, one-third as a man, and has spent thirteen years in his dotage. How old is Demochares?

SOME OLD ARAB AND HINDU PUZZLES

Other ancient civilizations, too, produced their share of mathematics and mathematical puzzles. The following two puzzles, one from the Arabic, the other from the Hindu tradition, both existed for centuries before they were ever written down.

6. **The Hungry Hunter** ☆☆

A hungry hunter chanced to meet two shepherds, one of whom had three small loaves, and the other five small loaves, all the loaves being of equal size. When the hunter asked them for food, they decided to divide the loaves equally among the three of them. The hunter thanked the shepherds and gave them eight piastres. How should the shepherds divide the money?

7. **The Dish of Potatoes** ☆☆

Three travellers stopped at a tavern and ordered a dish of potatoes for supper. When the landlord brought in the potatoes, the men were all asleep. The first of the travellers to awake ate a third of the potatoes and went back to sleep without disturbing his companions. The second traveller awoke, ate a third of the remaining potatoes and went back to sleep. A little later the third traveller did the same. When they were all three sleeping again, the landlord came in to clear the table and found eight potatoes left.

How many potatoes had the landlord provided initially?

SOME OLD FRENCH PUZZLES

The following five puzzles come from two French collections of mathematical problems, written by Chuquet in 1484 and by Clavius in 1608.

8. A Length of Cloth ☆

Out of a length of cloth one-third is black, one-quarter is bleached, and the remaining 3 yards are red. How long is the length of cloth?

9. A Man and His Money ☆

A man spends one-third of his money, and loses two-thirds of the remainder at dice, leaving 12 ducats in his pocket. How much money did he have originally?

10. The Value of a Cloak ☆

As wages for a year's work, a servant is promised 100 ducats and a cloak. The servant, however, leaves after only seven months, and receives the cloak and 20 ducats as his due.

How much is the cloak worth?

11. The Merchant ☆☆

A merchant visits three markets. At the first he doubles his money and spends 30 ducats. At the second he trebles his money and spends 54 ducats. At the third he increases his money fourfold and spends 72 ducats. If he has 48 ducats left, how much did he have to start with?

12. Customs Duties ☆☆

Two wine merchants arrive at the gates of Paris. One has 64 and the other 20 barrels of wine. Since they have not enough money to pay the customs duties, the first pays 40 francs and 5 barrels of wine, and the second pays 2 barrels of wine but receives 40 francs in change.

What is the value of each barrel of wine, and what is the duty payable on it?

PUZZLES OF LEWIS CARROLL

Lewis Carroll, the creator of *Alice In Wonderland*, was also Charles Lutwidge Dodgson, mathematician and logician. His puzzles bring together the strands of fantasy and logic, as is demonstrated by the following eleven puzzles.

13. A Stick I Found ☆

A stick I found that weighed two pound:
I sawed it up one day
In pieces eight of equal weight!
How much did each piece weigh?

(Everybody says 'a quarter of a pound', which is wrong.)

14. The Governor of Kgovjni ☆☆

The Governor of Kgovjni wants to give a very small dinner party, and invites his father's brother-in-law, his brother's father-in-law, his father-in-law's brother, and his brother-in-law's father. Find the number of guests.

15. Up Hill and Down Hill ☆☆

Two travellers spend from 3 o'clock till 9 in walking along a level road, up a hill, and home again: their pace on the level being 4 miles an hour, up hill 3, and down hill 6. Find the distance walked: also (within half an hour) the time of reaching the top of the hill.

16. A Circular Railway ☆☆☆

(a) Two travellers, starting at the same time, went opposite ways round a circular railway. Trains start each way every 15 minutes, the easterly ones going round in 3 hours, the westerly in 2. How many trains did each meet on the way, not counting trains met at the terminus itself?

(b) They went round as before, each traveller counting as 'one' the train containing the other traveller. How many did each meet?

17. Five Sacks ☆☆

There are 5 sacks, of which Nos. 1 and 2 weigh a total of 12 lbs; Nos. 2 and 3, 13½ lbs; Nos. 3 and 4, 11½ lbs; Nos. 4 and 5, 8 lbs; Nos. 1, 3 and 5, 16 lbs.
  Find the weight of each sack.

18. Scarves ☆☆

L makes 5 scarves, while M makes 2: Z makes 4 while L makes 3. Five scarves of Z's weigh one of L's; 5 of M's weigh 3 of Z's. One of M's is as warm as 4 of Z's; and one of L's as warm as 3 of M's.
  Which is best, giving equal weight in the result to rapidity of work, lightness and warmth?

19. A Spiral Walk ☆☆☆

An oblong garden, half a yard longer than wide, consists entirely of a gravel-walk, spirally arranged, a yard wide and 3,630 yards long. Find the dimensions of the garden.

20. Casualties ☆☆

If 70 per cent have lost an eye, 75 per cent an ear, 80 per cent an arm, 85 per cent a leg, what percentage, at least, must have lost all four?

21. Three Sons ☆☆

A man has three sons. At first, two of the ages are together equal to the third. A few years afterwards, two of them are together double the third. When the number of years since the first occasion is two-thirds of the sum of the ages on that occasion, one age is 21.
  What are the other two ages?

22. The Monkey and the Pulley ☆☆

A weightless and perfectly flexible rope is hung over a weightless, frictionless pulley attached to the roof of a building. At one end is a weight which exactly counterbalances a monkey at the other end.

If the monkey begins to climb, what will happen to the weight – will it remain stationary, will it rise or will it fall?

23. The Captive Queen ☆☆☆

A captive queen and her son and daughter were shut up in the top room of a very high tower. Outside their window was a pulley with a rope around it, and a basket fastened to each end of the rope of equal weight. They managed to escape with the help of this and a weight they found in the room, quite safely. It would have been dangerous for any of them to come down if they weighed 15 lbs more than the contents of the other basket, for they would do so too quick, and they also managed not to weigh less either.

The one basket coming down would naturally of course draw the other up.

The queen weighed 195 lbs, daughter 105, son 90, and the weight 75 lbs.

How did they all escape safely?

SAM LOYD

Sam Loyd (1841–1911) was America's (and possibly the world's) greatest creator of puzzles. He produced his first chess problem at the age of fourteen, and within a few years was acknowledged as the best in this field. For more than fifty years his puzzles appeared in countless newspapers and magazines. He also pioneered the use of puzzles as novelty advertising giveaways, demonstrating his unique blend of creativity and flair for publicity.

None of Loyd's puzzles appeared in book form during his lifetime. It was only after his death that his son, Sam Loyd Junior, collected his father's work to form the *Cyclopaedia of Puzzles*, which was published in 1914. The following eleven puzzles come from that mammoth opus.

24. The Stenographer's Salary ☆☆

Here is a problem from the ordinary affairs of life which is as interesting as it is puzzling to all who tackle it. The 'Boss' was feeling pretty good the other day, so he said to his stenographer:

'Now, Mary, in view of the fact that you never indulge in useless vacations, I have determined to raise your salary $100 every year. Beginning from today, for the ensuing year you will be paid weekly at the rate of $600 a year; next year at the rate of $700, the next at $800, and so on, always increasing $100 per year.'

'On account of my weak heart,' replied the grateful young woman, 'I suggest that it would be safer to make the change less abrupt. Start the salary from today on the basis of $600 a year, as suggested, but at the end of six months raise the yearly salary $25, and continue to give me a $25 yearly raise every six months, so long as my services are satisfactory.'

The boss smiled benignly upon his faithful employee as he accepted the amendment, but a twinkle in his eye set some of the boys to figuring whether or not the boss made a wise move by accepting her proposition. Can you tell?

25. Carnival Dice Game ☆☆

The following dice game is very popular at fairs and carnivals, but since two persons seldom agree on the chances of a player winning, I offer it as an elementary problem in the theory of probability.

On the counter are six squares marked 1, 2, 3, 4, 5, 6. Players are invited to place as much money as they wish on any one square. Three dice are then thrown. If your number appears on one die only, you get your money back plus the same amount. If two dice show your number, you get your money back plus twice the amount you placed on the square. If your number appears on all three dice, you get your money back plus three times the amount. Of course if the number is not on any of the dice, the operator gets your money.

A player might reason: the chance of my number showing on one die is 1/6, but since there are three dice, the chances must be 3/6 or 1/2, therefore the game is a fair one. Of course this is the way the operator of the game wants everyone to reason, for it is quite fallacious.

Is the game favorable to the operator or the player, and in either case, just how favorable is it?

26. Texas Drovers ☆☆

Three Texas drovers met on the highway and proceeded to dicker as follows.

Says Hank to Jim: 'I'll give you six pigs for a hoss; then you'll have twice as many critters in your drove as I will have in mine.'

Says Duke to Hank: 'I'll give you fourteen sheep for a hoss; then you'll have three times as many critters as I.'

Says Jim to Duke: 'I'll give you four cows for a hoss; then you'll have six times as many critters as I.'

From these interesting facts can you tell just how many animals were in each of the three droves?

27. Jack Sprat ☆☆☆

According to Mother Goose, Jack Sprat could eat no fat and his wife could eat no lean.

Together they could eat a barrel of fat pork in sixty days, whereas it would take Jack thirty weeks to perform this feat alone.

Together they could consume a barrel of lean pork in eight weeks, although his wife alone could not dispose of it in less than forty weeks.

Assuming that Jack would always eat lean pork whenever it was available and this his wife would do the same with fat, how long would it take both of them to eat a barrel of mixed pork, half fat and half lean?

28. The Leaning Tower of Pisa ☆☆☆

If an elastic ball is dropped from the Leaning Tower of Pisa at a height of 179 feet from the ground, and on each rebound the ball rises exactly one tenth of its previous height, what distance will it travel before it comes to rest?

29. The Shy Storekeeper ☆

'Give me three skeins of silk and four of worsted,' said little Susie as she placed 31 cents, the correct amount, on the counter.

As the storekeeper went to get the goods, Susie called out, 'I've changed my mind. I'll take four skeins of silk and three of worsted.'

'You're just one cent shy,' remarked the storekeeper as he placed the goods on the counter.

'Oh no,' said Susie as she picked up the goods and skipped out of the store. 'You are just one cent shy!'

What was the price of silk and worsted?

30. Carousel ☆

While enjoying a giddy ride on the carousel, Sammy propounded this problem: 'One-third of the number of kids riding ahead of me, added to three-quarters of those riding behind me gives the correct number of children on this merry-go-round.'

How many children were riding the carousel?

31. Mrs Wiggs' Cabbages ☆☆

Mrs Wiggs explained to Lovey Mary that she has a larger square cabbage patch now than she had last year and will therefore raise 211 more cabbages. How many of our mathematicians and agriculturalists can guess the number of cabbages Mrs Wiggs will raise this year?

32. How Wide Should the Strip Be? ☆☆

Farmers and laborers who have no great skills in mathematics will often solve, in a practical way, some very difficult problems. I call the attention of our puzzlists to the clever way in which a couple of farmers adjusted their affairs.

A Texas ranchman, who owned more land than he could conveniently farm, leased half of a certain field to a neighbor. This field was 2,000 yards long by 1,000 yards wide, but because of certain bad streaks which ran through the land it was decided that a fairer division would be obtained by cutting a band around the field than by dividing it in half.

I presume our puzzlists will find no great difficulty in determining the width of a border strip, to be cut all round that field, that will contain exactly half of the total crop. There is a simple rule which will apply to any rectangular field.

33. Quick Deal ☆☆

While the suburban boom is on, we will take occasion to tell how a real-estate speculator stopped off at a wrong station and, having a couple of hours to wait for the next train, made a quick and profitable deal. He bought a piece of land for $243 which he divided into equal lots, then sold them at $18 per lot, cleaning up the whole transaction before his train arrived. His profit on the deal was exactly equal to what six of the lots originally cost him.

How many lots were in that piece of land?

34. Sam Loyd's Boxes ☆☆☆☆☆

(Equipment: Sets for several of these games have been produced commercially, but you can make your own cardboard versions very simply.)

1. The 14–15 Box was probably Sam Loyd's most famous – and frustrating – creation:

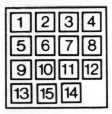

   As you can see, fifteen blocks are arranged in a square box in regular order, but with the 14 and 15 reversed. The game consists of moving the blocks about, one at a time, to bring them back to the present position in every respect except that the error in the 14 and 15 is corrected.

2. Once you have solved the original problem, have a go at this one. Start again with the blocks as in the original puzzle and move them so as to get the numbers in regular order, but with the vacant square at the upper left-hand corner instead of the lower right-hand corner.

3. This time, start with the blocks as before, but turn the box a quarter way round and move the blocks until they are as shown below.

	4	8	12
3	7	11	15
2	6	10	14
1	5	9	13

4. Finally, start as before, then shift the pieces until they form a magic square, the numbers adding to thirty along all vertical and horizontal rows, and the two diagonals.

5. In this box we have nine letters rather than fifteen numbers and the game begins with the box looking like this:

G	E	F
H	C	B
D		A

Now the aim of the game is this: moving one block at a time, restore the letters to their correct alphabetical order:

A   B   C

D   E   F

G   H

H. E. DUDENEY

Henry Ernest Dudeney (1847–1930) was England's greatest creator of puzzles, and the only contender with Sam Loyd for the world title. Dudeney and Loyd corresponded frequently during their lifetimes and were friendly rivals

35. Mistaking the Hands ☆☆☆

'Between two and three o'clock yesterday,' said Colonel Crackham, 'I looked at the clock and mistook the minute hand for the hour hand, and consequently the time appeared to be fifty-five minutes earlier than it actually was.' What was the correct time?

36. The Leap-year Ladies ☆☆☆

Last leap-year ladies lost no time in exercising their privilege of making proposals of marriage. If the figures that reached me from an occult source are correct, the following represents the state of affairs in this country.

A number of women proposed once each, of whom one-eighth were widows. In consequence, a number of men were to be married, of whom one-eleventh were widowers. Of the proposals made to widowers, one-fifth were declined. All the widows were accepted. Thirty-five forty-fourths of the widows married bachelors. One thousand two hundred and twenty-one spinsters were declined by bachelors. The number of spinsters accepted by bachelors was seven times the number of widows accepted by bachelors. Those are all the particulars that I was able to obtain. Now, how many women proposed?

37. Exploring the Desert ☆☆☆

Nine travellers, each possessing a car, meet on the eastern edge of a desert. They wish to explore the interior, always going due west. Each car can travel forty miles on the contents of the engine tank, which holds a gallon of fuel, and each can carry nine extra gallon cans of fuel and no more. Unopened cans can alone be transferred from car to car. What is the greatest distance at which they can enter the desert without making any depots of fuel for the return journey?

38. The Labourer's Puzzle ☆☆

Professor Rackbrane, during one of his rambles, chanced to come upon a man digging a deep hole.

'Good morning,' he said. 'How deep is that hole?'

'Guess,' replied the labourer. 'My height is exactly five feet ten inches.'

'How much deeper are you going?' said the professor.

'I am going twice as deep,' was the answer, 'and then my head will be twice as far below ground as it is now above ground.'

Rackbrane now asks you if you could tell how deep that hole would be when finished?

39. Mr Gubbins in a Fog ☆☆

Mr Gubbins, a diligent man of business, was much inconvenienced by a London fog. The electric light happened to be out of order and he had to manage as best he could with two candles. His clerk assured him that though both were of the same length one candle would burn for four hours and the other for five hours. After he had been working some time he put the candles out as the fog had lifted, and he then noticed that what remained of one candle was exactly four times the length of what was left of the other.

When he got home that night Mr Gubbins, who liked a good puzzle, said to himself, 'Of course it is possible to work out just how long those two candles were burning today. I'll have a shot at it.' But he soon found himself in a worse fog than the atmospheric one. Could you have assisted him in his dilemma? How long were the candles burning?

40. The Railway Station Clock ☆☆☆

A clock hangs on the wall of a railway station, 71 ft 9 in long and 10 ft 4 in high. Those are the dimensions of the wall, not of the clock! While waiting for a train we noticed that the hands of the clock were pointing in opposite directions, and were parallel to one of the diagonals of the wall. What was the exact time?

41. The Spot on the Table ☆☆☆

A boy, recently home from school, wished to give his father an exhibition of his precocity. He pushed a large circular table into the corner of the room, so that it touched both walls, and he then pointed to a spot of ink on the extreme edge.

'Here is a little puzzle for you, pater,' said the youth. 'That spot is exactly eight inches from one wall and nine inches from the other. Can you tell me the diameter of the table without measuring it?'

The boy was overheard to tell a friend, 'It fairly beat the guv'nor'; but his father is known to have remarked to a City acquaintance that he solved the thing in his head in a minute. I often wonder which spoke the truth.

42. The Fifteen Orchards ☆☆☆

In the county of Devon, where the cider comes from, fifteen of the inhabitants of a village are imbued with an excellent spirit of friendly rivalry, and a few years ago they decided to settle by actual experiment a little difference of opinion as to the cultivation of apple trees. Some said they wanted plenty of light and air, while others stoutly maintained that they ought to be planted pretty closely, in order that they might get shade and protection from cold winds. So they agreed to plant a lot of young trees, a different number in each orchard, in order to compare results.

One man had a single tree in his field, another had two trees, another had three trees, another had four trees, another five, and so on, the last man having as many as fifteen trees in his little orchard. Last year a very curious result was found to have come about. Each of the fifteen individuals discovered that every tree in his own orchard bore exactly the same number of apples. But, what was stranger still, on comparing notes they found that the total gathered in every allotment was almost the same. In fact, if the man with eleven trees had given one apple to the man who had seven trees, and the man with fourteen trees had given three each to the men with nine and thirteen trees, they would all have had exactly the same.

Now, the puzzle is to discover how many apples each would have had (the same in every case) if that little distribution had been carried out. It is quite easy if you set to work in the right way.

2. CHILD'S PLAY

43. ☆

If a brick weighs 9 lb and half a brick, what is the weight of a brick and a half?

44. ☆

Rearrange the following eleven letters to make just one word:
USTOODWERNJ

45. ☆

The windows on all four sides of my house face south. How is that possible?

46. ☆

Can you punctuate the following sentence in order to make sense of it?
SMITH WHERE JONES HAD HAD HAD HAD HAD HAD HAD HAD HAD HAD HAD THE EXAMINERS' APPROVAL

47. ☆

A man, looking at a portrait, said:
'Brothers and sisters have I none,
But this man's father is my father's son.'
What is the relationship between the speaker and the subject of the portrait?

48. ☆

When the day after tomorrow is yesterday, today will be as far from Sunday as today was from Sunday when the day before yesterday was tomorrow. What day is it?

49. ☆

Can you translate this:
YYURYYUBICURYY4ME

50. ☆

A frog at the bottom of a well climbs up 3 ft every day, but slips back 2 ft during the night. How long will he take to reach the top, if the well is 20 ft deep?

51. ☆

If it takes five men six hours to dig seven holes, how long does it take one man to dig half a hole?

52. ☆

Take the letters ERGRO. Put three letters in front of it, and put the same three letters after it, to form a common English word.

53. ☆

What is the next letter in this series?
    O T T F F S S . . .

54. ☆

Arrange the numbers from 1 to 9 in a square grid, as shown, so that each row and each column and the two main diagonals add up to 15.

55. ☆

Now arrange the numbers from 1 to 16 in a four by four square, so that each row and each column and the two main diagonals add up to 34.

56. ☆

Ken Tucky is 40. Louise Yanner is 13. How many years ago was Ken four times as old as Louise?

57. ☆

A combined collection of dogs and chickens has 43 heads and 120 feet. Of the collection, how many are dogs and how many are chickens?

58. ☆

If a third of six were three, what would the half of twenty be?

59. ☆

A farmer, when asked what number of animals he had, replied: 'They're all horses but two, all sheep but two, and all pigs but two.'
  How many animals had he?

60. ☆

  Three-fourths of a cross, and a circle complete,
  Two semi-circles at a perpendicular meet;
  Next add a triangle which stands on two feet,
  Two semi-circles and a circle complete.

What is being described in this verse?

61. ☆

Seven ears of corn are in a hollow stump. How long will it take a squirrel to carry them all out, if he carries out three ears a day?

62. ☆

A son asked his father how old he was, and received the reply: 'Your age is now one-quarter of mine, but five years ago it was only one-fifth.'
  How old is the father?

63. ☆

If it takes three minutes to boil one egg, how long will it take to boil two eggs?

64. ☆

What are the next two letters in this series:
  A E F H I K L M . . . . . .

65. ☆

What common chemical compound is represented by the following letters?
  H I J K L M N O

66. ☆

How many times does the letter S occur in the name of the longest river in the world?

67. ☆

What number gives the same result when it is added to 1½ as when it is multiplied by 1½?

68. ☆

How many times can you subtract the number 2 from the number 25?

69. ☆

What is the closest relation that your mother's brother's brother-in-law could be to you?

70. ☆

A man drives his car a certain distance at 60 mph and arrives at his destination one hour earlier than if he had driven at 50 mph. What was the distance?

71. ☆

A soldier is on parade and facing due west. The sergeant-major shouts at him:

       'Right turn!'
       'About turn!'
       'Left turn!'

In which direction is the soldier now facing?

72. ☆

    Mary had a tiny lamb,
    Its wool was pallid as snow,
    And any spot that Mary did walk
    This lamb would always go.
    This lamb did follow Mary to school,
    Although against a law;
    How girls and boys did laugh and play,
    That lamb in class all saw.
In what way is this odd? Think!

73. ✩✩

Two cyclists, twenty miles apart, start at the same instant and ride towards each other along a straight road at a speed of ten miles per hour. At the same instant a fly on the forehead of one of the cyclists starts to fly at fifteen miles per hour directly towards the other cyclist, lands on his forehead, and then flies back and forth over the continuously decreasing distance between the two cyclists until it is finally squashed as the foreheads of the two cyclists bump together.

How far has the fly flown, when all his journeys are added together?

74. ✩

There are three ordinary playing cards in a row. A diamond is on the left of a spade (though not necessarily next to it); an Eight is on the right of a King; a Ten is on the left of a heart; a heart is on the left of a spade.

What are the three cards?

75. ✩

If on January 1st you go to sleep at eight o'clock at night, having set your alarm clock to wake you at 9 a.m., and you sleep soundly until woken by the alarm, how many hours sleep will you get?

76. ✩

A tramp makes his own cigarettes from cigarette ends he collects. Seven ends will make a cigarette. He has collected 49 ends. How many cigarettes can he make from these?

77. ✩✩

Three missionaries and three cannibals have to cross a river. They have a boat, but it will only hold two people at a time. Cannibals must never be allowed to outnumber missionaries on either bank.

How do they get across the river?

78. ✩

Bill could never tell the truth. Tom could never tell a lie. One of them said, 'The other one said he is Bill.' Which one said that?

79. ✩

In a drawer there are five identical pairs of black socks and five identical pairs of brown socks, all jumbled together. If it was completely dark, how many socks would you need to take from the drawer to be sure of getting a matching pair?

80. ☆

There are five packets of sweets on a table. Four of the packets contain a total of 84 sweets. The fifth packet contains 4 sweets less than the average of the five packets.

How many sweets are there in the fifth packet?

81. ☆

Find a three-letter word which can go in front of any of the following words to form a new word.

TON   PET   ROT

82. ☆

Rearrange each of these words to form a girl's name:

ARMY   DINE   YACHT
TEAK   SAIL   IDEAL
YAM   HURT   AIRMAN

83. ☆

Rearrange each of these words to form a boy's name:

RICE   LINE   LYRIC
EEL   SAILS   NAILED
ANTS   EVENTS WANDER

84. ☆

The following words have had all their vowels removed. Can you work out what the words should be?

PL   A game played on horseback
PL   A game played on a table
NN   A vegetable
B   A musical instrument
KLL   A musical instrument
CLL   A musical instrument
CN   A type of boat
S   Relaxation

3. NUMBER PUZZLES

85. Pocket Money ☆☆

A father divided a certain number of pounds among his four children. To the first he gave a part, to the second one-third of what was left after the first's share, to the third he gave five-eighths of what was left, and to the fourth the balance, which equalled two-fifths of the first child's share. No child received as much as £20.

How much money did the father distribute, and how much did each child receive?

86. Boat Race ☆☆

In a time race, one boat is rowed over the course at an average of 4 yards per second, another moves over the first half of the course at the rate of 3½ yards per second, and over the last half at 4½ yards per second, reaching the winning post 15 seconds later than the first. Find the time taken by each.

87. 1105 ☆☆

The sum of the squares of two consecutive numbers is 1105. What are the two numbers?

88. Division ☆☆

Divide 100 into two parts, so that a quarter of one exceeds one-third of the other by 11.

89. Find Three Numbers ☆☆

Find three numbers such that the first with half of the other two, the second with one-third of the other two, and the third with one-fourth of the other two, shall each be equal to 34.

90. Strange Squares ☆☆☆

The square of 45 is 2025. If we split this in two, we get 20 and 25. 20 plus 25 is 45 – the number we started with.

Find two other numbers with four-digit squares that exhibit the same peculiarity.

91. December and May ☆☆

An old man married a young woman. Their combined ages amounted to 100. The man's age multiplied by 4 and divided by 9 gives the woman's age.

What were their respective ages?

92. A Walking Expedition ☆☆

Jim and Bill set out on a walking expedition at the same time – Jim from X to Y, and Bill from Y to X.

On reaching Y, Jim immediately sets off back to X. Now, Jim reaches Y four hours after meeting Bill, but he reaches X three hours after their second meeting. In what time did each perform the journey?

93. Banker's Order ☆☆

A man went into a bank with exactly $1000, all in $1 bills. He gave the money to a cashier and said, 'Put this money into ten bags in such a way that if I call and ask for any number of dollars up to $1000, you can give me the exact amount by handing over one or more bags, without having to open any of the bags.'

How was the cashier to comply with these instructions?

94. Paintings by Numbers ☆☆

An art dealer has a certain number of paintings for sale. He sells half the paintings and one more to one customer, half the remainder and one more to a second customer, half the remainder and one more to a third customer, half the remainder and one more to a fourth customer – by which time he has sold all the paintings. How many had he?

95. Groceries ☆☆

My five grocery items each weighed a whole number of ounces, and the total weight was less than two pounds. With a balance scale, I found the following three inequalities, and in each case, the addition of the banana to the lighter side turned it into the heavier side.
   (a) tomato and apple together failed to balance the orange.
   (b) apple and orange together failed to balance the tomato.
   (c) tomato and orange together failed to balance the potato.
I also found the following instances of equality:
   (d) apple balanced the banana and tomato together.
   (e) tomato and potato together balanced the other three items.
What was the weight of each item?

96. State of the Poll ☆☆☆

In a constituency in which each elector may vote for two candidates, half of the constituency vote for A, but divide their votes among B, C, D and E in the proportion of 4, 3, 2, 1. Half the remainder vote for B, and divide their votes between C, D, E in proportion 3, 1, 1. Two-thirds of the remainder vote for D and E, and 540 do not vote at all.
   Find the state of the poll, and the number of electors.

97. A Certain Number ☆☆☆

There is a certain number consisting of three digits which is equal to 36 times the sum of its digits. 7 times the leftmost digit plus 9 is equal to 5 times the sum of the remaining digits. 8 times the second digit minus 9 is equal to the sum of the first and third.
   What is the number?

98. Rope ☆☆

A man ordered a length of rope by telephone, but when he went to collect it he found that the assistant had miswritten the order by interchanging feet and inches. As a result, the rope was only 30 per cent of the length that the man wanted.
   What length of rope did he order?

99. A Powerful Number ☆☆☆☆

There is a certain number whose third and fourth powers, taken together, use all the digits from 0 to 9, each once and once only. What is the number?

100. Pairs of Weights ☆☆☆

With a pair of each of four different weights, any whole number of pounds from 1 pound up to 170 pounds can be weighed. What are the weights?

101. Four Dresses ☆☆☆

A woman has four dresses for which she paid a total of £80. The first dress cost as much as the second plus half of the third. The second cost as much as the fourth minus the cost of the third. The third cost one-third of the first. The fourth cost as much as the second and third together.

What was the price of each dress?

102. What is the Number? ☆☆

There is a certain number such that the square of its half is equal to the number with its digits reversed. What is the number?

103. Gamblers ☆☆

Three gamblers – Abe, Bert and Cal – sit down to play cards. As a result of the first game, Abe lost to each of Bert and Cal as much money as they started the game with. In the second game Bert lost similarly to each of Abe and Cal. And in the third game – you guessed it – Cal lost similarly to each of Abe and Bert. Each man then had $40.

How much money had each man when they started to play?

104. Escalation ☆☆☆

On one of the escalators on the London Underground, I find that if I walk down 26 steps I need 30 seconds to get to the bottom; but if I make 34 steps then I need only 18 seconds to reach the bottom.

If the time is measured from the instant that the top step begins to descend to the time I step off the last step at the bottom on to the level platform, what is the height of the stairway in steps?

105. Fours and Fives ☆☆☆

Find the smallest number that, when divided by 45, 454, 4545 and 45454, leaves the remainders 4, 45, 454 and 4545 respectively.

106. Going Home ☆☆☆

My friend Alex, who lives in the country, caught an earlier train home than usual yesterday. His wife normally drives to the station to meet him. But yesterday he set out on foot from the station to meet his wife part way. He reached home 12 minutes earlier than he would have done had he waited at the station for his wife. The car travels at a uniform speed which is five times Alex's speed on foot. Alex reached home at exactly six o'clock. At what time would he have reached home if his wife, forewarned of his change of plan, had met him at the station?

107. Life Spans ☆☆☆

The life span of a whale is 4 times that of a stork, which lives 85 years longer than a guinea pig, which lives 6 years less than an ox, which lives 9 years less than a horse, which lives 12 years longer than a chicken, which lives 282 years less than an elephant, which lives 283 years longer than a dog, which lives 2 years longer than a cat, which lives 135 years less than a carp, which lives twice as long as a camel, which lives 1,066 years short of the total of all the creatures' life spans.

What is the life span of each creature?

108. Circuits ☆☆☆

David and Jonathan start together from the same point on a circular path and walk round, each at his own pace, until both arrive together at the starting point.

If David performs the circuit in 3 minutes 44 seconds and Jonathan in 6 minutes 4 seconds, how many times does each go round the path?

109. 365 ☆☆☆

If we multiply 64253 by 365 we get the product 23452345, where the first four digits are repeated. What is the largest number that can be multiplied by 365 to produce a similar product of eight digits with the first four digits repeated in the same order? There is no objection to a digit being repeated within the first four.

110. Coaches ☆☆

A coach operator, not having room in his garage for eight of his coaches, increased the size of his garage by 50%, and then had room for eight more coaches than the number he owned.
How many coaches did he own?

111. Loading a Cart ☆☆

If a man can load a cart in ten minutes, and a friend can load it in five minutes, how long will it take them both to load it, working together?

112. Measuring Sticks ☆☆

A measuring stick, 13 inches long, needs only four marks on it so that it can measure any whole number of inches from 1 to 13. The marks are at the 1, 2, 6 and 10 inch positions. From 0 to 1 measures 1 inch, from 0 to 2 measures 2 inches, from 10 to 13 measures 3 inches, from 2 to 6 measures 4 inches and so on.
On a measuring stick 36 inches long, what is the smallest number of marks needed so that it can measure any whole number of inches from 1 to 36? And where should the marks be placed?

113. Burning the Candle at Both Ends ☆☆

One-third of an hour after a candle was lighted, the other end was also lighted. It took a further one-third of an hour for the candle to burn out. If the candle was lighted at both ends at the start, and one end was extinguished when only the middle one-third of the candle remained, how long in all would it take to burn the candle out?

114. Ferry-Boats ☆☆☆

Two ferry-boats start at the same time from opposite sides of a river, travelling across the water on routes at right angles to the shore. Each boat travels at a constant speed, though their two speeds are different. They pass at a point 720 yards from the nearest shore. Both boats remain at their slips for ten minutes before starting back. On the return trips, they meet 400 yards from the other shore.

How wide is the river?

115. Find Two Numbers ☆☆☆

Find two numbers such that the square of the first plus the second equals 11, and the square of the second plus the first equals 7.

116. Wine and Water ☆☆☆

There are two barrels, one of which holds thirty gallons more than the other. The larger barrel is filled with wine and the smaller one with water.

Ten gallons are drawn from each barrel. That from the first barrel is poured into the second, and vice versa. Each barrel is shaken thoroughly to mix the contents. Again ten gallons are taken from each barrel, and that from each is poured into the other.

If the larger barrel now contains thirteen gallons of water, what is the total capacity of the smaller barrel?

117. Palindromic Pairs ☆☆☆

Did you know that certain pairs of two-digit numbers have the same product when both numbers are reversed? For example:

$$12 \times 42 = 24 \times 21$$
$$12 \times 63 = 36 \times 21$$
$$12 \times 84 = 48 \times 21$$
$$23 \times 96 = 69 \times 32$$
$$24 \times 63 = 36 \times 42$$
$$24 \times 84 = 48 \times 42$$
$$26 \times 93 = 39 \times 62$$
$$46 \times 96 = 69 \times 64$$

There are six other sets of numbers of this nature. How many can you find?

118. A Way to Weigh ☆☆☆

Five children found a method of getting themselves all weighed on an automatic weighing machine with just one coin. Two of them got on the stand at the same time, and one child changed places with another until all the ten possible pairs had been weighed. The weights, in pounds, were as follows: 114, 115, 118, 119, 121, 122, 123, 125, 126 and 129. Can you work out their individual weights?

119. One to Nine ☆☆☆

A puzzle which has long been popular is to place plus and minus signs, wherever one cares to, between the digits 1, 2, 3, 4, 5, 6, 7, 8 and 9 so as to make the resulting expression equal in value to 100. The digits must remain in the original sequence. A typical solution is:

$$12 + 3 - 4 + 5 + 67 + 8 + 9 = 100$$

In this solution, six plus and minus signs were used. Can you find another solution, using the fewest possible signs?

120. Nine to One ☆☆☆

This is similar to the previous problem, the difference being that the digits have to be in the sequence 9, 8, 7, 6, 5, 4, 3, 2, 1. Here is one typical solution:

$$98 + 7 - 6 + 5 - 4 + 3 - 2 - 1 = 100$$

But the aim is to find a solution using the fewest possible plus and minus signs.

121. A Question of Age ☆☆

A man and his wife had three children – John, Ben and Mary. The difference between the parents' ages was the same as between John and Ben and between Ben and Mary. The ages of John and Ben, multiplied together, equalled the age of the father, and the ages of Ben and Mary multiplied together equalled the age of the mother. The combined ages of the family amounted to ninety years.

What was the age of each person?

122. The Bag of Nuts ☆☆

Three boys were given a bag of nuts, and they agreed to share out the nuts in proportion to their ages, which together amounted to 17½ years. The bag contained 770 nuts, and for every four nuts Joe took, Jack took three, and for every six that Joe took, Jim took seven.

How many nuts did each boy take, and what are their respective ages?

123. Strange Multiplication ☆☆☆

If I multiply 51,249,876 by 3 (thus using all the nine digits once and once only) I get 153,749, 628 (which again contains all the nine digits once).

Similarly if I multiply 16,583,742 by 9, the result is 149,253,678.

Now, take 6 as your multiplier and try to arrange the remaining eight digits so as to produce by multiplication a number containing each of the nine digits.

124. Curious Numbers ☆☆☆☆

The number 48 has this peculiarity, that if you add 1 to it, the result is a square number (49, the square of 7) and if you add 1 to its half, you also get a square number (25, the square of 5).

Can you find the next three smallest possible numbers that also have this peculiarity?

125. Find a Square ☆☆☆

What is the smallest square number that ends with the greatest possible number of identical non-zero digits?

126. Pandigital Fractions ☆☆☆

Using all the digits from 1 to 9 (each digit being used once and once only) it is possible to form a fraction equal in value to a half, thus:

$$\frac{6729}{13458}$$

Using these nine digits, see if you can form fractions equal in value to:

(a) a third

(b) a quarter
(c) a fifth
(d) a sixth
(e) a seventh
(f) an eighth
(g) a ninth

127. Four Primes ☆☆☆

A, B, C and D represent four different digits such that ADDD, AACA, BCDB and BDAC are prime numbers.
  What digits do the letters represent?

128. ABCD ☆☆☆

Once again, A, B, C and D represent four different digits. These digits may be combined in different ways to give 24 different four-digit numbers. These 24 numbers include:

Four prime numbers
7 products of two odd primes
1 square of a prime
8 numbers divisible by 2, but not by 4
2 numbers divisible by 4, but not by 8
1 number divisible by 8, but not by 16
1 number divisible by 16

What are these numbers?

CRYPTARITHMETIC

In the following five puzzles, each letter represents a different digit. Your task is to discover which digit each letter represents.

129. Send More Money ☆☆

$$
\begin{array}{r}
SEND \\
MORE \ + \\
\hline
MONEY
\end{array}
$$

130. Sixty ☆☆

```
            T E N
            T E N
        F O R T Y  +
        ─────────
        S I X T Y
```

131. Scrabble ☆☆

```
      L E T T E R S
    A L P H A B E T  +
    ───────────────
    S C R A B B L E
```

132. Not Red Jam ☆☆

$$\frac{N O T}{3} = M E \qquad \frac{R E D}{6} = M E \qquad \frac{J A M}{9} = M E$$

133. Presidential ☆☆

```
      L Y N D O N
              B  ×
      ─────────
    J O H N S O N
```

134. A Long Division ☆☆☆

See if you can reconstruct this long division, given only one of the digits. There is a unique answer.

```
              * 7 * * *
          ┌─────────────
* * * │ * * * * * * * *
          * * * *
          ─────────
            * * *
            * * *
            ─────────
          * * * *
          * * *
          ─────────
              * * * *
              * * * *
```

4. CIRCLES, SQUARES AND ANGLES

135. Cross Cut 1 ☆☆

Divide a cross, such as that shown in the diagram, into four pieces with two straight cuts, so that the pieces may be put together to form a perfect square.

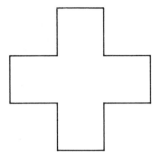

136. Cross Cut 2 ☆☆

Can you divide this shape into four pieces, identical as to size and shape, so that the pieces may be put together to form a perfect square?

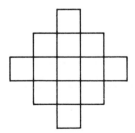

137. Seven Lines ☆☆☆

What is the largest number of non-overlapping triangles that can be produced by drawing seven straight lines? The diagram shows how seven lines can produce six non-overlapping triangles, but you ought to be able to find a much better solution than this.

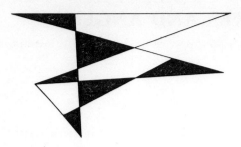

138. Folding a Triangle ☆☆☆

Given a perfectly plain square piece of paper, how would you fold it so as to form the largest possible equilateral triangle? The triangle with sides equal in length to the sides of the square, as shown in the diagram, will not be the largest possible. No markings or measurements may be made except by the creases themselves.

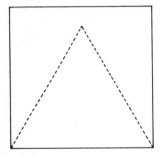

139. Folding a Hexagon ☆☆☆

You are given a perfectly plain square sheet of paper. How would you fold it so as to make creases that will form a regular hexagon, as shown in the diagram? You are not permitted use of a ruler or a pencil or any other instrument whatever.

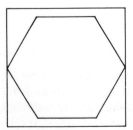

140. The Side of a Square ☆☆

How long is the side of a square whose area is equal to twice the sum of its sides?

141. A Strange Island ☆☆☆

There is an island in the form of a semi-circle. Two men start from a point on the diameter; one walks along the diameter, and the other at right angles to it. The former reaches the extremity of the diameter after walking 4 miles, and the latter the boundary of the island after walking 8 miles. Find the area of the island.

142. The Crescent Puzzle ☆☆☆☆

The crescent is formed by two circles, and C is the centre of the larger circle. The width of the crescent between B and D is 9 inches, and between E and F 5 inches. What are the diameters of the two circles?

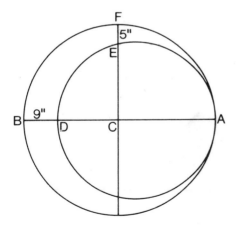

143. The Six-Sided Field ☆☆☆

A farmer owns a field in the shape of a regular hexagon, each side being 40 yards in length. He has a donkey tethered by a rope 50 yards long which is fastened to a post in one corner of the field.

How many square yards of the field may the donkey graze over?

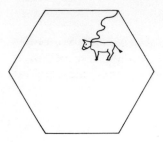

144. The Garden Path ☆☆☆☆

A man has a rectangular garden, 55 yards by 40 yards, and he makes a diagonal path, one yard wide, exactly in the manner indicated in the diagram. What is the area of the path?

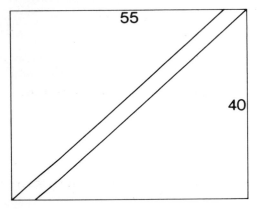

(Note that the width of the path is exaggerated in the diagram for the sake of clarity.)

145. A Triangular Question ☆☆☆

A right-angled triangle has sides that are all a whole number of inches. One of the sides is 47 inches long. What are the lengths of the other two sides?

146. The Ladder ☆☆☆

A ladder was fastened against a high wall of a building. A man unfastened it and pulled it out four yards at the bottom. It was then found that the top of the ladder had descended just one-fifth of the length of the ladder. What was the length of the ladder?

147. The Bell Rope ☆☆☆

A bell rope, passing through the ceiling above, just touches the belfry floor, and when you pull the rope to the wall, keeping the rope taut, it touches a point just three inches above the floor, and the wall was four feet from the rope when it hung at rest.

How long was the rope from floor to ceiling?

148. Dividing a Garden ☆☆

Mr Budd has a square garden, containing twelve trees, as in the illustration.

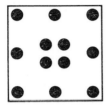

How may he divide his garden into four parts, all identical as to size and shape, so that each part contains three trees?

149. Quartering the Circle ☆☆☆

With three lines of equal length it is very easy to divide a circle into three equal parts, as shown here:

The problem, however, is to divide a circle into *four* equal parts, using three lines of equal length. The lines do not have to be straight, but they must not cross.

150. The Potato Puzzle ☆☆☆

Take a circular slice of potato, place it on the table, and see into how many pieces you can divide it with six cuts of a knife. Of course you must not readjust the pieces or pile them after a cut. What is the greatest number of pieces you can make?

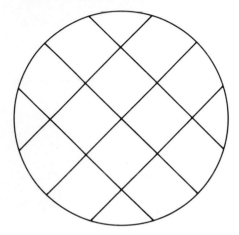

The illustration shows how to make sixteen pieces. This can, of course, be easily beaten.

151. Splitting a Horseshoe ☆☆

With two straight-line cuts, can you divide a horseshoe, such as that illustrated, into six pieces?

152. The Carpet-Fitter's Problem ☆☆☆

A carpet-fitter had a piece of carpet shaped like this:

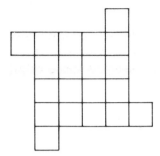

How could he cut it into four pieces, so that they could be rearranged to form a square?

153. The Joiner's Problem ☆☆☆

A joiner has a piece of wood as shown in the diagram.

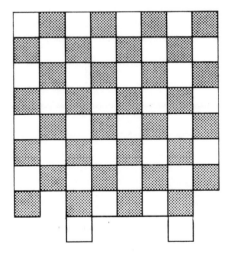

How can he cut it into only two pieces that can be fitted together to form a chessboard?

154. The Dressmaker's Problem ☆☆☆

A dressmaker has a piece of checkered cloth with four buttons attached, as illustrated here.

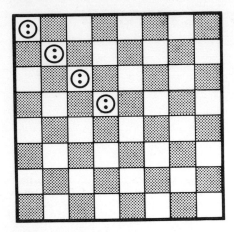

How can she cut it into four pieces, identical as to size and shape, each piece to contain one button?

155. Star-Maker ☆☆☆

You are given an octagonal shape with an octagonal hole in the middle.

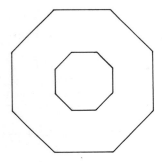

The problem is to cut it into eight pieces, all identical as to size and shape, which can be put together again to form an eight-pointed star, again with an octagonal hole in the middle.

156. Cigarette Boxes ☆☆☆

A manufacturer sends out his cigarettes in boxes of 160. They are packed in eight rows of 20 each, and exactly fill the box. Could he, by packing differently, get more than 160 into the box? If so, what is the greatest number that he could add? At first sight it sounds absurd to expect to get more cigarettes into a box that is already exactly filled, but a moment's consideration should give you the key to the paradox.

5. THREE-DIMENSIONAL PUZZLES

COIN PUZZLES

157. Coin Triangle ☆☆

Arrange ten coins in the form of a triangle, as shown in the diagram.

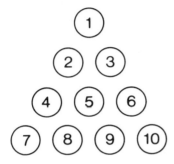

Now turn the triangle upside down by moving just three of the coins.

158. Eight in a Row ☆☆

Place eight coins in a row, the first four showing heads and the last four showing tails.

In four moves – each move consisting of moving two adjacent coins to a new position – you have to rearrange the coins so that the heads and tails are alternating. You are not allowed to turn over any of the coins, and when you have finished you must not be left with any gaps in the row.

159. Seven-Coin Rounders ☆☆

Place seven coins, all heads up, in a circle. Starting from any coin, count 1, 2, 3 in a clockwise direction and turn the third coin over. Repeat the process, beginning from any of the coins that are still heads up. Continue until all but one of the coins are tails up.

160. Five Rows ☆☆

Take ten coins and arrange them in five rows with four coins in each row.

161. Nine Rows ☆☆☆

Take twenty-seven coins and arrange them in nine rows with six coins in each row.

162. Twelve Rows ☆☆☆

Take thirteen coins and arrange them in twelve rows with three coins in each row.

163. Twenty-One Rows ☆☆☆

Take twenty-two coins and arrange them in twenty-one rows with four coins in each row.

164. Star Trek ☆☆☆

On a sheet of paper draw an eight-pointed star, and number the points as shown in the diagram. Place a coin heads up on point 1, another coin

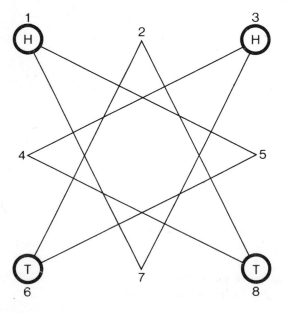

heads up on point 3, a coin tails up on point 6, and another coin tails up on point 8.

The puzzle is to transfer the two coins that are heads up to the points occupied by the coins that are tails up, and vice-versa. You are allowed seven moves. You may only move one coin at a time, although in each move you may move the coin along one line to a vacant point, or along more than one line in succession provided that the coin rests in a vacant point at the end of each line.

MATCH PUZZLES

165. Leave Three Triangles ☆☆

Arrange twelve matches as shown in the diagram.

Now move four matches so as to leave just three equilateral triangles.

166. Twelve Matches ☆☆☆

For each of these little problems start with twelve matches laid out like this:

(a) Move two matches and make seven squares.
(b) Move three matches and leave three squares.
(c) Move four matches and leave two squares.
(d) Move four matches and leave three squares.
(e) Move four matches and make ten squares.
(f) Remove two matches so as to leave two squares.

167. Match Spiral ☆☆

With thirty-five matches form a spiral as shown in the diagram.

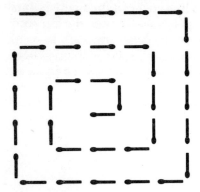

Now transform the spiral into three squares by moving just four of the matches.

DOMINO PUZZLES

The oldest known set of dominoes was discovered in 1922 in the tomb of King Tutankhamen of Egypt (c. 1371–c. 1352 BC) and can be seen today

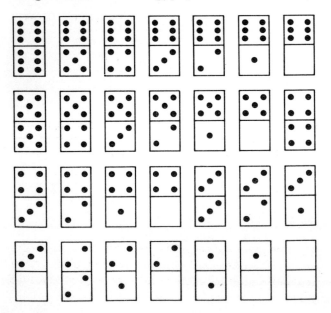

in the Tutankhamen Museum in Cairo. It seems generally agreed that dominoes actually originated in China and were introduced into Europe by Venetian traders in the fourteenth or fifteenth century AD. From Italy they were introduced into France, and it is believed that the English first learned about dominoes from French prisoners-of-war during the Napoleonic Wars at the beginning of the nineteenth century.

Dominoes are rectangular tiles, made usually from bone, ivory, wood or plastic. A standard European set consists of 28 tiles. The face of each tile is divided by a central line into two equal squares, each of which is either blank or marked with pips from one to six in number. This set is also known as the Double-6 set, as the double-6 is the top domino in the set. All the puzzles here are played with this set.

168. Six Square ☆☆

Take the 6 lowest dominoes in the set – the 0/0, the 0/1, the 0/2, the 1/1, the 1/2 and the 2/2 – and arrange them in a square, so that each side of the square contains the same number of pips.

169. Six Rectangle ☆☆

Using the same 6 dominoes as in the previous puzzle, form a rectangle, so that each of the four sides of the rectangle contains the same number of pips.

170. Ten Square ☆☆

Using the 10 lowest dominoes in the set – all the dominoes up to the double-3 – form a square, so that the number of pips on each side of the square is the same and so that none of the joins match.

171. Three Rectangles ☆☆☆

Using the 15 lowest dominoes in the set – all the dominoes up to the double-4 – form 3 separate rectangles of 5 dominoes each so that each of the 12 sides (that is to say, all 4 sides of each of the 3 rectangles) contain the same number of pips.

172. Five Lines ☆☆☆

Using the same 15 dominoes as in the last puzzle, form 5 lines, with 3 dominoes in each line, so that in each of the 5 lines the joins match and there are exactly the same number of pips in each line.

PENTOMINOES

Pentominoes were introduced to the world by a Californian mathematician, Solomon W. Golomb, in an article published in the *American Mathematical Monthly* in 1954.

Starting from the definition of a domino as two squares 'simply connected' (i.e. joined along their edges) he coined the word polyomino to describe the class of shapes formed by squares connected in this way. A monomino is a single square, a domino 2 squares simply connected, a tromino 3 squares, a tetromino 4 squares, a pentomino 5 squares, a hexomino 6, and so on.

From the family of polyominoes, it is the pentomino which has attracted the most interest because of its considerable recreational potential.

There are twelve distinct ways in which five squares can be joined together to form a pentomino. These twelve shapes constitute a set of pentominoes, which can either be bought from a shop or made at home. The twelve pieces in the set look like this:

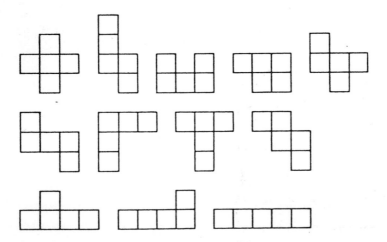

These pentominoes form the basis of a number of interesting puzzles.

173. Pentomino Puzzles ☆☆☆☆

(a) Using any four pentominoes, form a 4 by 5 rectangle.
(b) Using any five pentominoes, form a 5 by 5 square.
(c) Using any six pentominoes, form a 5 by 6 rectangle.
(d) Using any seven pentominoes, form a 5 by 7 rectangle.
(e) Using any eight pentominoes, form a 4 by 10 rectangle.
(f) Using any nine pentominoes, form a 3 by 15 rectangle.
(g) Use all twelve pentominoes to form a 4 by 15 rectangle.

174. A Square with a Hole ☆☆☆

Using all twelve pentominoes, form an 8 by 8 square with a 2 by 2 square hole in the centre.

175. Pentomino Triplication ☆☆☆☆

Select any one of the pentominoes. Using nine of the remaining pentominoes form a large-scale version of the selected pentomino, each dimension being three times greater than the original.

CHESS PROBLEMS

176. ☆☆☆

These five classic chess problems are all the work of Sam Loyd. See if you can solve them.

(a) How can White play and mate on his third move at the latest, against any black defence?

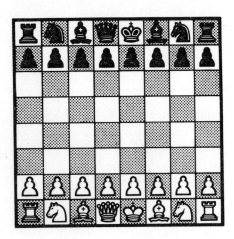

(b) If both sides make exactly the same moves, how can White mate in four? See if you can find both the possible solutions.

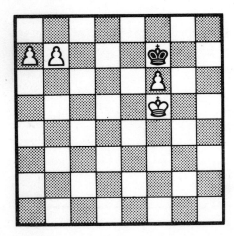

(c) How can White play and force mate on his third move, against any black defence?

(d) How can White play and force mate on his third move, against any black defence?

(e) (i) Place the black king where he would be stalemated.
     (ii) Place the black king where he would be checkmated.
     (iii) Place the black king where he would be checkmated next move.
     (iv) Place the black king on a square where he can never be checkmated.

SOLITAIRE PUZZLES

The *Solitaire* board is normally made of wood or plastic and has 33 holes to hold the pieces, which are usually small marbles or pegs. (The French board has 37 holes, and is hexagonal in shape.)

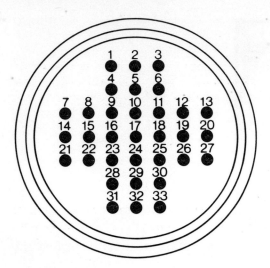

There are a number of puzzles for the solitaire board, but the method of making moves is common to all of them. A counter may be moved only by jumping it over a neighbouring counter to a vacant space directly on the other side. The counter which was jumped over is then removed from the board. Jumps may be made only horizontally or vertically — diagonal moves are not permitted.

The number of jumps made in a game of solitaire equals the number of counters removed. However, a series of consecutive jumps made at one time with a single counter can be regarded as a single move; hence a player can aim not merely at solving a given puzzle but also at finding the solution that requires the minimum number of moves.

177. The Latin Cross ☆☆

Start with six counters forming the shape of a cross, filling holes 5, 9, 10, 11, 17 and 24. The object is to remove five counters in five moves and leave the remaining counter in the centre of the board (hole 17).

178. The Greek Cross ☆☆

Start with nine counters arranged in the form of a cross, filling holes 5, 10, 15, 16, 17, 18, 19, 24 and 29. The object is to remove eight counters and leave the remaining counter in the centre of the board (hole 17). It is possible to do this in six moves.

179. The Triangle ☆☆☆

For this puzzle you start with sixteen counters forming a triangle over holes 5, 9, 10, 11, 15, 16, 17, 18, 19 and 21–27. Can you reduce this formation to a solitary counter in the centre of the board? Can you do it in eight moves?

180. The Square ☆☆☆☆

Start with the board set out as for standard solitaire – all the squares occupied, except the central one (17). The aim is to finish with eight counters left on the board, in the form of a square, occupying holes 9, 10, 11, 16, 18, 23, 24 and 25.

6. LOGIC PUZZLES

181. One Question ☆☆

A hiker comes to a fork in the road and doesn't know which way to go to reach his destination. There are two men at the fork, one of whom always tells the truth while the other always lies. The hiker doesn't know which is which, though. He may ask one of the men only one question to find his way. Which man does he ask, and what is the question?

182. The Missing Dollar ☆☆

Three men registered in a hotel and asked for three separate rooms at ten dollars each, so the clerk received thirty dollars from the three men. The next day the clerk found that these three rooms should have been let for twenty-five dollars instead of thirty dollars, so he called the page boy and gave him the five dollars rebate to give back to the three men. The boy, however, who was not very honest, gave the men one dollar each and kept two dollars for himself. This meant that each man, instead of paying ten dollars, actually paid nine dollars. This makes twenty-seven dollars for the three men; the page boy had two dollars; 27 plus 2 equals 29, so where did the other dollar go?

183. King Arthur's Knights ☆☆☆

King Arthur sat at the Round Table on three successive evenings with his knights – Beleobus, Caradoc, Driam, Eric, Floll and Galahad – but on no occasion did any person sit next to anyone who had sat next to him before. On the first evening they sat in alphabetical order round the table. But afterwards King Arthur arranged the two next sittings so that he might have Beleobus as near to him as possible and Galahad as far away from him as could be managed. How did he seat the knights to the best advantage, remembering that rule that no knight may have the same neighbour twice?

184. Mary's Age ✩✩☆

The combined ages of Mary and Ann are 44 years, and Mary is twice as old as Ann was when Mary was half as old as Ann will be when Ann is three times as old as Mary was when Mary was three times as old as Ann.
How old is Mary?

185. Shunt ✩✩☆

A locomotive, L, is on the main line of a railway. The trucks, marked 1 and 2 in the diagram, are on sidings which meet at the points, where there is room for one truck only but not for the locomotive.

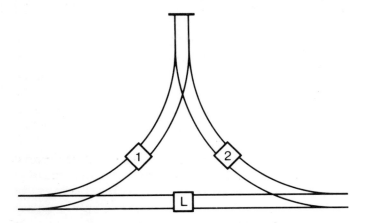

The problem is to swap the positions of the two trucks and leave the locomotive in its original position on the main line. The locomotive may push or pull the trucks — it may go between them, pulling one and pushing the other — but no truck may move without the locomotive.

186. The Eight Engines ✩✩☆

The diagram represents the engine-yard of a railway company under eccentric management. The engines are allowed to be sationary only at the nine points indicated, one of which is at present vacant. It is required to move the engines, one at a time, from point to point, in seventeen moves, so that the engines shall be in numerical order round the circle, with the central point left vacant. But one of the engines has had its fire

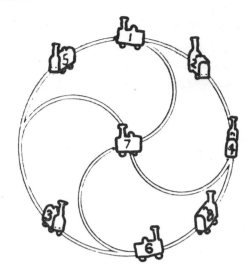

drawn and therefore cannot move. How is the thing to be done? And which engine remains stationary throughout?

hairdresser receptionist *Judy.*
Jennifer Jane redhead
blonde ; brunette typist

187. Bathing Beauties ☆☆☆

Of the three finalists in the bathing beauty contest, Jane is older than the redhead, but younger than the hairdresser. Judy is younger than the blonde, while Jennifer is older than the brunette. The typist is the receptionist's younger sister.

Can you give the hair-colouring and profession of each girl in order of age?

188. Weight Lifters ☆☆☆

Boris, Sergei, Tam and Viktor are weight lifters. Viktor can outlift Tam, but Sergei can outlift Viktor. Tam can outlift Boris, but Sergei can outlift Tam. Therefore:

(a) Both Boris and Sergei can outlift Viktor.
(b) Viktor can outlift Boris but can't outlift Tam.
(c) Viktor can outlift Boris by more than he can outlift Tam.
(d) None of the above.

Which of these is correct?

189. A Game of Cards ☆☆☆

Dwight had been playing cards with three of his friends. Thinking about the game afterwards, he recalled these facts:

1. Ambrose and Bertram had better scores than the doctor.
2. Ambrose first dealt to Bertram, then to Mr Hooper, then to the accountant, and then to himself.
3. In the last hand, Bertram dealt to the priest, to Mr Hooper, to Clint, and then to himself.
4. Mr Eastwood went home before Clint did.
5. The doctor had a better score than Mr Grimm.
6. Mr Fuller went home before the priest.

With these facts, sprinkled with a little logical deduction, you ought to be able to work out who was who. For example, what were the musician's first and last names?

*Ann
dancer*   *Barbara*

190. Take Four Girls ☆☆☆

MissG

1. Ann is younger than the dancer, who lives directly west of Barbara.
2. The dancer lives directly north of Miss Green, who lives exactly five miles from Cathy, who lives exactly two miles from the singer.
3. The pianist is older than Miss White and Diana is older than the actress.
4. Cathy is older than Miss Brown, who lives exactly three miles from Barbara, who lives directly south of Miss Black.

How far does Diana live from Ann? And which of the four girls is the oldest?

191. The Triple 'A' Club ☆☆☆

The membership of the Triple 'A' Club is drawn from three professions — auditors (who always tell the truth), advertising men (who always lie), and actors (whose statements are alternately true and false, or false and true).

Although I am not a member, I have occasion to visit the club from time to time. Here is what happened on four of my recent visits.

(a) I was introduced on one occasion to three new members, one being from each profession. Their names were John, Paul and George. Each of them made two statements as follows:

John:	'I am not an advertising man'.
	'Paul is not an actor'.
Paul:	'I am not an advertising man'.
	'George is not an auditor'.
George:	'I am not an advertising man'.
	'John is not an actor'.

What was the profession of each new member?

(b) On another occasion I met three members, a representative of each profession, whose names were Tom, Dick and Harry. When I enquired about their professions and ages, each made two statements as follows:

Tom:	'Harry is an auditor'.
	'Dick is older than Harry'.
Dick:	'Harry is an actor'.
	'Harry is older than Tom'.
Harry:	'Tom is an advertising man'.
	'Tom is older than Dick'.

What is the profession of each member, and how do their ages compare?

(c) On yet another occasion I asked three members, one from each profession, about their earnings. Their names were David, Lloyd and George, and each made two statements as follows:

David:	'I am an actor'.
	'I earn more than George'.
Lloyd:	'I am an auditor'.
	'I earn more than David'.
George:	'I am an advertising man'.
	'I earn more than Lloyd'.

What is the profession of each member and how do their earnings compare?

(d) The club committee consists of three members, one from each profession, who fill the roles of chairman, secretary and treasurer. The present committee members are Freeman, Hardy and Willis. I asked two of them about the composition of the committee, and this is what they told me:

Freeman:	'I am not an actor'.
	'Hardy is not the chairman'.
Hardy:	'I am not an auditor'.
	'Willis is not the secretary'.

Can you name the person who fills each post on the committee, and identify his profession?

192. Islands in the Sun ☆☆☆

In the Gulf of Lug there are five islands, each with a different number of inhabitants. A different language is spoken on each island (reflecting the chequered colonial past of the area), and each island's economy is based on a different exported commodity.

From the facts below, see if you can work out the details of each island's population, language and export.

1. Cetri has 1 million inhabitants.
2. The island which exports bananas has a smaller population than the island on which Dutch is spoken.
3. The island on which Spanish is spoken does not export precious stones.
4. The island which exports coffee has a population of 2 million.
5. Auni's population is double that of the island on which English is spoken.
6. The island which exports emeralds has a population of 5 million.
7. Bebi is not the island with 3 million inhabitants.
8. The population of the island which exports amethysts is half that of the island on which French is spoken.
9. Equin has 1 million fewer inhabitants than the island which exports dates.
10. Dequar's 4 million inhabitants outnumber the population of the island on which Portuguese is spoken.

193. Do It Yourself ☆☆☆

On my bookshelves I have five books concerned with do-it-yourself subjects. From the facts below, see if you can work out the title and author of each book, the colour of its cover and the number of pages it contains.

(Note: the name of an author is not a reliable guide to the name of the book written by that author.)

1. *Painting and Decorating* has 50 more pages than the book with the white cover.
2. The book by Walter Wall has a blue cover.
3. The book by Bernard Cole has 20 more pages than *Domestic Insulation*.
4. *Carpet Fitting* does not have a blue cover.
5. The book with the yellow cover has 170 pages.
6. The book by Matt Coates has 70 fewer pages than the book with the green cover.

7. *Improve Your Garden* has 300 pages.
8. *Indoor Heating* was written by Celia Holmes.
9. The book with the white cover has 190 pages.
10. The book by Anita Lawn has a red cover and 220 pages.

194. Lewis Carroll's Symbolic Logic ☆☆☆

In each of these problems by Lewis Carroll, you have to find the 'ultimate conclusion' that can be drawn from the statements given. You do this by taking any two statements with a common term and seeing what conclusion can be drawn from them. Combine the result with another statement that has a term in common and draw another conclusion from them. Continue in this way until you reach the final conclusion that can be drawn – this will be the same no matter in which order you combine the statements.

Perhaps an example will make the process clearer. Take the following statements:

a. There are no pencils of mine in this box.
b. No sugar-plums of mine are cigars.
c. The whole of my property, that is not in this box, consists of cigars.

From (a) and (c) we may conclude 'All my pencils are cigars'. Combining this result with statement (b), we obtain the ultimate conclusion that 'No pencils of mine are sugar-plums'.

1   a. No acrobatic feats, that are not announced in the bills of a circus, are ever attempted there.
     b. No acrobatic feat is possible, if it involves turning a quadruple somersault.
     c. No impossible acrobatic feat is ever announced in a circus bill.

2   a. No birds except ostriches are 9 feet high.
     b. There are no birds in this aviary that belong to any one but me.
     c. No ostrich lives on mince-pies.
     d. I have no birds less than 9 feet high.

3   a. No interesting poems are unpopular among people of real taste.
     b. No modern poetry is free from affectation.
     c. All your poems are on the subject of soap-bubbles.
     d. No affected poetry is popular among people of real taste.
     e. No ancient poem is on the subject of soap-bubbles.

4 a. I call no day 'unlucky', when Robinson is civil to me.
  b. Wednesdays are always cloudy.
  c. When people take umbrellas, the day never turns out fine.
  d. The only days when Robinson is uncivil to me are Wednesdays.
  e. Everybody takes his umbrella with him when it is raining.
  f. My 'lucky' days always turn out fine.

5 a. Animals are always mortally offended if I fail to notice them.
  b. The only animals that belong to me are in that field.
  c. No animal can guess a conundrum unless it has been properly
   trained in a Board-School.
  d. None of the animals in that field are badgers.
  e. When an animal is mortally offended it always rushes about
   wildly and howls.
  f. I never notice any animal unless it belongs to me.
  g. No animal that has been properly trained in a Board-School ever
   rushes about wildly and howls.

6 a. The only animals in this house are cats.
  b. Every animal is suitable for a pet, that loves to gaze at the moon.
  c. When I detest an animal, I avoid it.
  d. No animals are carnivorous, unless they prowl at night.
  e. No cat fails to kill mice.
  f. No animals ever take to me, except what are in this house.
  g. Kangaroos are not suitable for pets.
  h. None but carnivora kill mice.
  i. I detest animals that do not take to me.
  j. Animals that prowl at night always love to gaze at the moon.

7. VISUAL PUZZLES

195. Distances ☆☆☆

Which is the greatest distance: from A to B or from B to C?

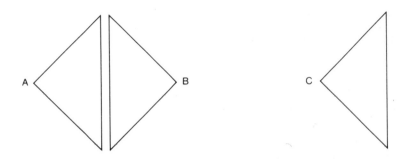

196. Arcs ☆☆

If the circle represented by arcs A, B and C were completed, which would have the greatest diameter?

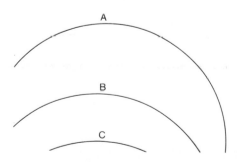

197. A Curious Cube ☆☆

(a) Is the cube viewed from above or below?
(b) Is the line across the corner of the cube straight or bent?

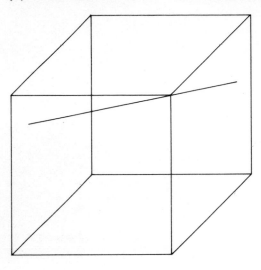

198. Two Lines ☆☆

Which line is the longer: AC or BD?

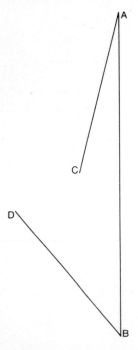

199. Three Lines ☆☆

Which of these three lines is the longest: the top one, the middle one or the bottom one?

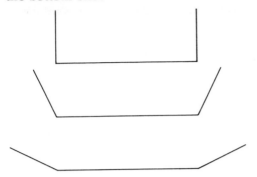

200. Five Shapes ☆☆

Which of these five shapes is the largest and which is the smallest?

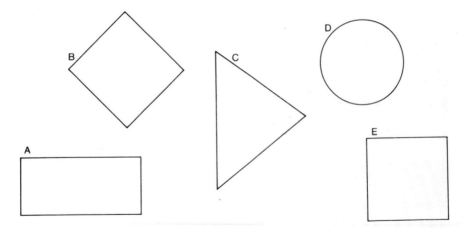

201. Two Circles ☆☆

Which of the two circles is the larger?

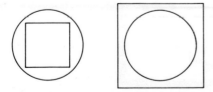

202. Horizontals ☆☆

Which of the two horizontal lines is longer, the top one of the bottom one?

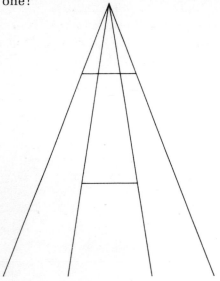

203. The Cretan Labyrinth ☆☆

The first and the best-known of all the ancient mazes was the Cretan Labyrinth designed by Daedalus as a devilish den for the famous Minotaur. Theseus slew the Minotaur and made his escape from the labyrinth. He used some thread of course, provided by Ariadne.

You're not so lucky. Start at the centre of the labyrinth and see if you can find your way out. This maze is very simple, as long as you can stop your eyes playing tricks with you.

204. The Somerton Maze ☆☆

At Somerton in Oxfordshire, there is a turf path one foot wide and twelve hundred feet long, constructed as shown in the diagram below.

Most mazes are easier to trace on paper than they are on the ground. But in this case, although it is very simple to follow the actual turf path, tracing the route on paper is rather more difficult.

It is the *dark* line you have to follow. See if you can trace it to the centre.

205. Crossings ★★★

You cannot get to the centre of this maze without crossing some lines. What are the least number of lines you need to cross to get from B to A?

206. The Philadelphia Maze ★★★★

This maze is the creation of H. E. Dudeney, who posed the question: how many ways are there to the centre?

(CAUTION: It is reported that one person who tried to solve this puzzle drove himself to the point of insanity and took his own life!)

207. **Trick Donkeys** ☆☆☆

This is one of the most famous puzzles of Sam Loyd.
   If the puzzle is cut along the dotted lines, how can the three pieces

be arranged — without folding — so that the two jockeys ride the two donkeys?

TANGRAM PUZZLES

Tangrams are an ancient form of puzzle from China. A tangram set consists of seven pieces, formed by dissecting a square as shown in the diagram.

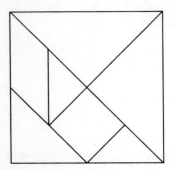

The object of a tangram puzzle is to arrange the seven pieces to form a specified shape. All the pieces must be used, and no piece may overlap another.

208. Tangram Teasers ☆☆☆

See if you can make each of these shapes with the seven tangram pieces.

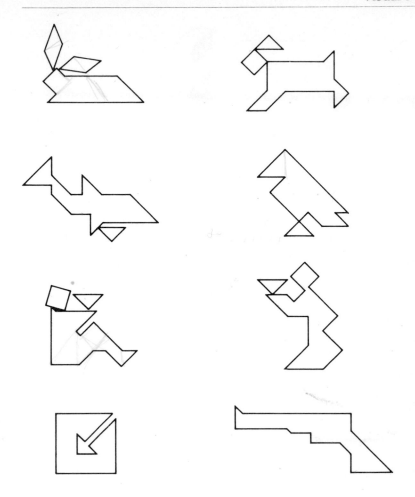

209. Tangram Digits ☆☆☆

Arrange the tangram pieces to make each of the digits from 1 to 8, as shown.

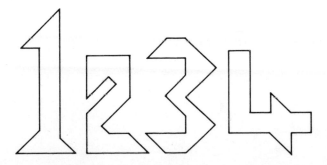

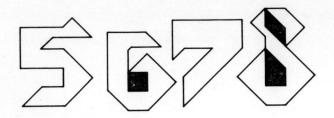

210. Two Tangram Gentlemen ☆☆☆

In this puzzle by H. E. Dudeney, the two gentlemen seem to be identical except that one has a foot which the other lacks. Yet both figures were made using all seven pieces of the tangram set, with no pieces overlapping.

Can you create each of the two figures with the tangram pieces?

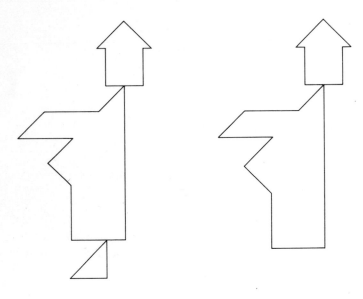

8. WORDPLAY

211. Double Meanings ☆☆

Find a single word which may mean the same as either word in the pair.
For example, the answer to THROW ACTORS would be CAST.
1. Clever pain. *Smart*
2. Produce whip. *Crop*
3. Support couple. *Brace*
4. Contrary talk. *Converse*
5. Impartial goal. *Objective*
6. Absolute state. *Utter*

212. Palindromes ☆☆

The solution to each clue is a palindromic word (one that is the same when read from right to left as from left to right).
1. Wisecrack.
2. Action.
3. Twelve.
4. Former Middle-East rulers.
5. Made into a god.
6. Principle.

213. Letter Transplants ☆☆

Form each pair of words into a pair of synonyms by transplanting a single letter from one word into the other. For example, POTION and PIERCE would become PORTION and PIECE.
1. OAK & WEST.
2. TINE & BID.
3. FOG & BLEAT.
4. AGE & RANGER.
5. SHEAR & CAR.
6. AID & SCOUR.
7. RAVER & ASSET.
8. LAVE & QUITE.
9. SPINY & GRATE.
10. FLIT & CROQUET.

214. A Common Property ☆☆

The verbs BRING, BUY, CATCH, FIGHT, FREIGHT, SEEK, TEACH and THINK share a common property that no other common verbs in the English language possess. What is it?

215. Double Letters ☆☆☆

There are several letters which frequently occur as doubles in English words. Double L, double T, and double S are all very common. But can you find words containing the following doubled letters?

　　HH　II　KK　UU　VV　WW

Your answers might be very obscure words, but they need not be – our answers are all perfectly common words in everyday use.

216. Words of Note ☆☆☆

Using the musical notes C, D, E, F, G, A, and B, what is the longest word that can be played on a piano? That is, using any of these letters, as many or as few times you like, but using no other letters, what is the longest word you can find? No foreign or hyphenated words, please.

217. Triple Word Squares ☆☆☆

A word square is an arrangement of words one below another in the form of a square so that they read the same horizontally and vertically.

　　Below are the clues for three such word squares. There's just one snag – the three sets of clues have been shuffled together, and you have to work out which clue belongs to which word square. To help you the central letters have already been inserted.

1. Group of eight; Delight; Striped quadruped.
2. Illegal activity; Mistake; Midday meal
3. Bury; Weary; Fetch.
4. Musical composition; View; Correct.
5. Termagant; Inert gas; Toy bear.

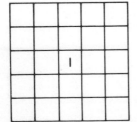
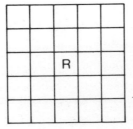
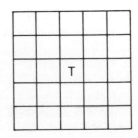

218. Rhyme Time ✩✩✩

The ten words and expressions given here (some of which are French) all
rhyme with NO, and yet each ends with a different letter of the alphabet:

DOUGH   WOE   OHO
WHOA   DE TROP   APROPOS
SOL   ROW   BON MOT
GATEAU

Now, can you find as many words and expressions as possible, ending
with different letters of the alphabet, that rhyme with the word SAY?
You may use the French language, and you should be able to find ten or
more.

219. Anagrams Plus C ✩✩

By adding a C to each of the words below, then shuffling the letters, it is
possible to form a new word. Add another C, shuffle again, and a third
word appears. For example, by adding C to ESAU, you can create
CAUSE. Add another C, and you have ACCUSE.

See how many you can solve, avoiding plurals and verbs ending in
S.

OIL   TAPE   HERE   LEAN   LOUT
HAT   OUST   NEAR   HATE   SPITE
ARK   OAST   SEAR   HEAD   NOSE
IRK   ROSE   SOUR   RILE   NEAT

220. Three Riddles ✩✩✩

(a) My first is in BORDER and also in BED;
     My second's in ROLL but never in BREAD;
     My third is in MILE but isn't in METRE;
     My fourth's found in PINT but not found in LITRE;
     My fifth's not in PAIN but always in ACHE;
     My sixth is in PIE but never in CAKE;
     My seventh is found both in ANKLE and KNEE;
     My whole is a creature that swims in the sea.

(b) My first is in SUGAR but is not in SWEET;
     My second's in WARMTH but isn't in HEAT;
     My third is found not in HILLS but in DALES;
     While my fourth is seen in RIVETS not NAILS;
     My fifth's in FIANCEE and also in WIFE;

And my sixth appears both in TROUBLE and STRIFE;
My seventh's in LADY but never in LORD;
My whole is a force that can't be ignored.

(c) My first is in LADY but isn't in MAN;
My second's in TIN but is not in CAN;
My third is found both in SCOTLAND and WALES;
My fourth is in HILLS as well as in DALES;
My fifth is in BLUE but is not in BLACK;
My sixth is in PARCEL and also in PACK;
My seventh's in SHOUT but isn't in SHREIKING;
My whole may be heard, in a manner of speaking.

221. Two Double Riddles ☆☆☆

Each of these riddles has two equally correct answers – you have to find both.

(a) My first is in SPLIT but is not in TEAR;
My second's in APPLE and also in PEAR;
My third is in BITTER but is not in SOUR;
My fourth is in MOMENT but is not in HOUR;
My fifth is in QUADRANT as well as in SQUARE;
My sixth is in CIRCUS but is not in FAIR;
My seventh's in SHINE and also in SHEEN;
My whole, you will see, has leaves that are green.

(b) My first is in RABBIT but is not in HARE;
My second's in BRACE but is not in PAIR;
My third is in LADDER but is not in CLIMB;
My fourth is in LEMON and also in LIME;
My fifth is in AUNT but is not in NIECE;
My sixth is in GANDER but is not in GEESE;
My seventh is seen both in GRANDMA and DAUGHTER;
My whole is an island surrounded by water.

222. American Names ☆☆☆

Which state of the USA does TINA come from? Well, it could be either norTh carolINA or wesT virgINiA, because both these states contain the letters of her name in the correct sequence.

Here are ten more names. See if you can find their states of origin.
(a) EVA   (f) RHODA
(b) MAE   (g) DIANA
(c) ALAN   (h) SYLVIA
(d) ANTON (i) DEAN
(e) NESTA   (j) SHARON

223. Linkwords ☆☆☆

The clues, which are in random sequence, define eight five-letter words. Solve the clues, and then insert the answers one below another in the diagram in the correct sequence so that each word differs from the preceding word by only one letter.

The first and last letters have been inserted to guide you.

(a) Depart

Animal

Weighty

Brag

Hire

Shore

Hoist

Minimum

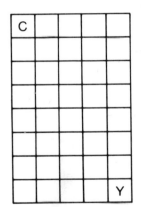

(b) Chest

Fetch

Dense

Inebriated

Lorry

Edge

Ruse

Beverage

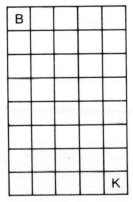

224. Confusibles ☆☆☆

This puzzle consists of pairs of words which are quite different in meaning but are frequently confused with each other. For example, FLAUNT and FLOUT, LUXURIANT and LUXURIOUS. See how many of the ten pairs you can identify.

(a) A hospital for the treatment of chronic diseases
     An institution for the promotion of health
(b) To reveal
     To depreciate
(c) Beggary
     Dishonesty
(d) To command solemnly
     To renounce
(e) To irritate or scrape
     To censure or reprimand
(f) To rout
     To make uneasy
(g) Corrupt
     Pardonable
(h) To write or compose
     To charge with a crime
(i) Self-pleased
     Pleasing to others
(j) Occurring every two years
     Occurring twice a year

225. Consecutive Letters ☆☆☆

The word ABSCOND contains the four consecutive letters ABCD, in the correct order. Indeed the word ABSCONDED contains the letters ABCDE. See if you can find words that contain the following groups of letters in the correct order.

   DEFG   FGHI   HIJK   MNOP   QRST   RSTU   XYZ

226. Alphabetical Shifts ☆☆☆

Consider the word COLD. If you shift each letter forward three positions in the alphabet, C becomes F, O becomes R, L becomes O, and D becomes G – so you end up with a new word, FROG.

Similarly, BALK can be turned into ONYX by shifting each letter forward 13 positions in the alphabet.

We have performed a similar process on 10 five-letter words. How rapidly can you work backwards from the words given here, and determine what words we started with?

(a) BEEFS   (f) FERNS
(b) INGOT   (g) JOLLY
(c) LORRY   (h) TOFFS
(d) SORRY   (i) TIFFS
(e) FREUD   (j) TIGER

227. Word Patterns ☆☆☆

(a) There are 52 distinct patterns which can be displayed by five-letter words. For example, SATIN, with no repeated letters, has the pattern 12345; TRUTH, having the first and fourth letters the same, has the pattern 12314; RACER, having the first and fifth letters the same, has the pattern 12341; and LEVEL, having the first and fifth letters the same, as well as the second and fourth, has the pattern 12321.

See if you can find examples for the following patterns:

12344	12213	12323	12131
11232	12231	12331	12311
12123	12233	12332	12232
12132	12312	11231	12322
12133	12313	12113	12112

(b) Examples of patterns of six-letter words are:

SENSES	= 123121	TITBIT	= 121321
HUBBUB	= 123323	MAMMAL	= 121123
SETTEE	= 123322	ACACIA	= 121231

Now see if you can find words displaying the following patterns:

123232	122323	121133	123123
123321	122131	122321	123212
122132	121223	123443	123344

228. Typewriter Words ☆☆☆

(a)   Q W E R T Y U I O P
          A S D F G H J K L
          Z X C V B N M

This is the order in which letters appear on a standard typewriter keyboard. ASH, RUG and TUG are three words whose letters occur in 'typewriter order'. Can you find longer examples? What is the longest such word you can find? Doubled letters (as in TOO) are acceptable.

(b)   What is the longest word that can be typed using just the letters on the top row of the typewriter keyboard – Q, W, E, R, T, Y, U, I, O, P? QUIRE and PEPPER are two examples, but no doubt you will be able to find longer words than these.

(c)   What is the longest word that can be typed using just the letters on the second row of the typewriter keyboard – A, S, D, F, G, H, J, K and L?

229. A,E,I,O,U ☆☆☆☆

(a)   FACETIOUS is one English word which contains the five vowels A,E,I,O,U in the correct sequence, each vowel occurring once and only once. Can you think of another common English word which shares this property?

(b)   There are, of course, many other words containing one occurrence of each of the five vowels, but in a different order. See if you can think of a word containing the five vowels in each of the sequences shown below:

AIEOU   OEAUI   AUIOE   AIOUE   EOUAI
IOUAE   EUOIA   EUAIO   OAUIE   OUEAI
UAIOE   UOIAE

230. Headliner ☆☆☆

There are many words which form another word when the initial letter is removed. The pairs of clues for the columns in this puzzle refer to such words.

One clue defines the whole word; the other clue defines the word that is formed when the initial letter of the first word is removed. Either clue may come first in the pair.

For example, if the clue was 'Correct; shining' the answer would be B-RIGHT.

If you complete all the columns correctly, the headline formed by the initial letters will spell out the name of a famous person.

Column 1. SUFFER; PRISON.
Column 2. ASSENTED; AVARICE.
Column 3. IN GOOD TIME; ALMOST.
Column 4. MOVEMENT; FEELING.
Column 5. AFT; SEVERE.
Column 6. MORE CERTAIN; MONEY-LENDER.
Column 7. WITHOUT DIFFICULTY; SUGGEST.
Column 8. DIFFICULTIES; FOREIGN CURRENCY.
Column 9. ODD; ALIENATE.
Column 10. TIDY; DINE.

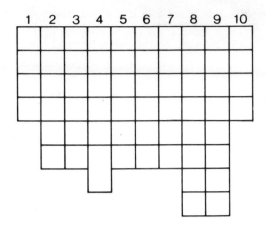

231. Single-Word Anagrams ☆☆☆

If you were asked to provide a single-word anagram of PARTISAN, it should not take you too long to find the answer ASPIRANT. See how long it takes you to find a single-word anagram for each of the following words:

(a) TREASON	(i) ESTIMATING
(b) OBEYING	(j) CONSIDERATE
(c) BESTIARY	(k) EXCITATION
(d) ASSAYING	(l) LEGISLATOR
(e) MASCULINE	(m) CENTRALISE
(f) DICTIONARY	(n) INCONSIDERATE
(g) BARGAINED	(o) CEPHALOMETRIC
(h) CATECHISM	(p) VICEPRESIDENTS

CHARADES

If you have ever played the party game of Charades (or seen it played as a panel game on TV) you will know what to expect here. A piece of verse defines a word – firstly syllable by syllable ('my first', 'my second', etc.) and then the whole word ('my whole'). You have to guess the word being thus defined.

Here are two examples of the genre, which reached the height of its popularity in the late Victorian period.

232. Beside the Brook ☆☆

Beside the brook one summer day
  When Nature all was merry,
I saw a gypsy maiden stray,
  As brown as any berry;
She with the limpid waters quenched her thirst,
And picked a simple salad of my *first*.

The woodbine and the eglantine,
  The woodruff and the mallow,
Delight to twine and intertwine
  Beside that streamlet shallow;
And kissed by sunlight and caressed by dews,
My *second* in the air around diffuse.

The sun went down, the twilight fell,
  Outshone the stars unnumbered;
Each floweret closed its honeyed cell,
  And nature softly slumbered.
While pale and cold across the heavens stole,
In modest maiden majesty, my *whole*.

233. Rifle Practice ☆☆

It was a gallant Volunteer,
  And he went forth to shoot;
He always went the bull's-eye near,
  And hit thrice to boot;
And he was clearly not the worst
  Who aimed his rifle at my *first*.

And while the yards they fired were few,
  Upon his feet stood he;
But when the distance greater grew,
  He knelt upon his knee;
And when the widest space was reckoned,
  He lay down flat upon my *second*.

Within the hut the marker stood,
  To score down every shot;
He signalled those whose aim was good,
  And those whose aim was not;

When to the bull's-eye bullets whirred,
   He bade the red flag do my *third*.

Awakened by the early spring,
   And taking little heed,
A poor unhappy giddy thing
   Went straying o'er the mead,
And so got shot! Your tears control,
   'Twas not a child — 'twas but my *whole*.

234. An Enigma ☆☆

A word there is of plural number,
Foe to ease and tranquil slumber;
Any other word you take
And add an S will plural make.
But if you add an S to this,
So strange the metamorphosis;
Plural is plural now no more,
And sweet what bitter was before.

This enigma was composed by the British Prime Minister George Canning (1770–1827).

235. Queen Victoria's Acrostic ☆☆☆

This puzzle is said to have been composed by Queen Victoria to entertain the royal children — presumably, on this occasion she *was* amused.

If you solve the clues correctly, the initial letters will be found to spell out the name of a town in England, and the final letters, read upwards, will spell out what that town is famous for.

1. A city in Italy
2. A river in Germany
3. A town in the United States
4. A town in the United States
5. A town in Holland
6. The Turkish name for Constantinople
7. A town in Bothnia
8. A city in Greece
9. A circle on the globe

236. Doublets ☆☆☆

This type of puzzle was invented by Lewis Carroll. Here he describes the puzzle in his own words:

'The rules of the puzzle are simple enough. Two words are proposed, of the same length; and the puzzle consists in linking these together by interposing other words, each of which shall differ from the next word *in one letter only*. That is to say, one letter may be changed in one of the given words, then one letter in the word so obtained, and so on, till we arrive at the other given word. The letters must not be interchanged among themselves, but each must keep its own place. As an example the word "head" may be changed into "tail" by interposing the words "heal, teal, tell, tall". I call the two given words "a Doublet", the interposed words "Links", and the entire series "a Chain", of which I here append an example:

```
H E A D
h e a l
t e a l
t e l l
t a l l
T A I L
```

'It is, perhaps, needless to state that it is *de rigueur* that the links should be English words, such as might be used in good society.'

You should now be ready to tackle the following Doublets.

3 Links
(a)   Change WET to DRY
(b)   Cover EYE with LID
(c)   Make EEL into PIE
(d)   Prove RAVEN to be MISER
(e)   Change OAT to RYE
(f)   Make TEA HOT

4 Links
(g)   Drive PIG into STY
(h)   Change FISH to BIRD
(i)   REST on SOFA

5 Links
(j)   Dip PEN into INK
(k)   Touch CHIN with NOSE
(l)   Change TEARS into SMILE
(m)   PITCH TENTS

(n)   Turn POOR into RICH
(o)   Evolve MAN from APE
(p)   Make FLOUR into BREAD
(q)   Get COAL from MINE
(r)   Stow FURIES in BARREL

6 Links
(s)   Make WHEAT into BREAD
(t)   Raise FOUR to FIVE
(u)   Make HARE into SOUP
(v)   Prove PITY to be GOOD
(w)   Make BLACK WHITE
(x)   Run COMB into HAIR
(y)   WHIP LASH
(z)   Sell SHOES for CRUST
(aa)   Make BREAD into TOAST

7 Links
(bb)   STEAL COINS
(cc)   Get WOOD from TREE
(dd)   Prove GRASS to be GREEN
(ee)   Change ELM into OAK
(ff)   Combine ARMY and NAVY
(gg)   Place BEANS on SHELF
(hh)   BUY an ASS
(ii)   Raise ONE to TWO

8 Links
(jj)   Change CAIN into ABEL
(kk)   Change BLUE to PINK

9 Links
(ll)   Pay COSTS in PENCE
(mm)   Put LOAF into OVEN
(nn)   Make KETTLE HOLDER

10 Links
(oo)   Prove ROGUE to be BEAST
(pp)   QUELL a BRAVO
(qq)   Trace RIVER to SHORE

12 Links
(rr)   Turn WITCH into FAIRY

237. Find the States ☆☆☆

Enter the answers to the cryptic clues (all five-letter words) in the diagram. The columns containing the first and last letters of the answers will then spell out the names of two American states. Then rearrange the letters contained in the shaded squares to give the name of a third American state.

1. Now his tricks include a game of cards.
2. Is little Susan having children?
3. It's an odd mark.
4. Fowl with headdress on.
5. The weight of a wild cat.
6. Fasteners at one's fingertips.
7. Mistakes with underwear.
8. Harden in river.
9. Scandinavian boatmen or seafarers take part.

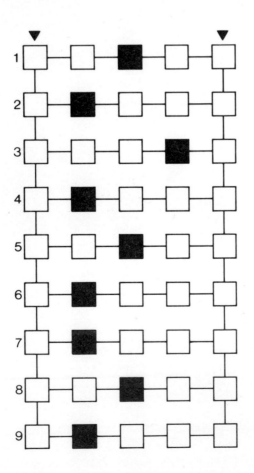

9. CROSSWORDS AND FRIENDS

(the spellings in the answers to the clues that follow are American or English according to the nationality of the compiler)

238. The Original Crossword ☆☆☆

The world's first crossword was published in the newspaper *The New York World* in December 1913. It was the work of Arthur Wynne, an expatriate Liverpudlian. Here it is:

2-3	What bargain hunters enjoy.
4-5	A written acknowledgement.
6-7	Such and nothing more.
10-11	A bird.
14-15	Opposed to less.
18-19	What this puzzle is.
22-23	An animal of prey.
26-27	The close of a day.
28-29	To elude.
30-31	The plural of is.
8-9	To cultivate.
12-13	A bar of wood or iron.
16-17	What artists learn to do.

20-21	Fastened.
24-25	Found on the seashore.
10-18	The fibre of the gomuti palm.
6-22	What we all should be.
4-26	A day dream.
2-11	A talon.
19-28	A pigeon.
F-7	Part of your head.
23-30	A river in Russia.
1-32	To govern.
33-34	An aromatic plant.
N-8	A fist.
24-31	To agree with.
3-12	Part of a ship.
20-29	One.
5-27	Exchanging.
9-25	To sink in mud.
13-21	A boy.

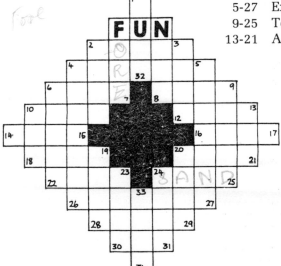

239. The Crossword Clown ☆☆☆

This crossword was published by H. E. Dudeney in 1925.

We give a portrait of our old friend, the Clown. The words defined begin at the numbers and go horizontally or vertically, as the case may be, and stop at the blacked-out squares. Every blank square has to be filled with a letter.

HORIZONTAL

1   A fruit.
4   A boat.
6   Conflict.
8   'An excellent substitute for butter'.
10   For example.
11   A drink beheaded.
12   Answers.
17   A knot.
18   A throw.
19   A sail.
20   Therefore.
22   Either.
23   An English county.
29   A well-known boxer.
30   A poet.

VERTICAL

1   To cultivate.
2   A youngster.
3   The mark.
4   A conveyance.
5   A period.
6   A conveyance.
7   Ideal gardens.
8   Military dinners.
9   A season of the Church.
13   'The' in foreign language.
14   Exclamation of disgust.
15   A congealed liquid.
16   A grain.
21   Surmounts.
22   Slang for all correct.
24   Belongs to.
25   A tear.
26   From.
27   Open.
28   Behold.

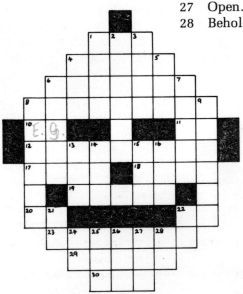

240. The Alphabet ✩✩✩

Here is another unusual crossword by H. E. Dudeney.

The point of this crossword is that every one of the twenty-six letters of the alphabet is used once and only once. We give the definitions, but do not indicate the locations of the words or their direction, horizontal or vertical.

DEFINITIONS

A metal. Parts of trees. To annoy. Whim or imagination. A sign, example. What person or persons. A man's shortened Christian name. To puzzle or make sport of.

241. Knock Knock ✩✩✩✩

Edward Powys Mathers produced crosswords for *The Observer*, under his pseudonym of Torquemada, from 1926 until 1939. He is acknowledged to be one of the founding fathers of the cryptic crossword as we know and love it today. Here is one of his typically entertaining creations.

To save space it must be imagined that each italic clue has been prefaced by the first player saying 'Knock Knock', the second saying 'Who's there?' and the first replying with a given-name. In the clue itself the second player asks 'Given-name who?' and the first player amplifies his previous answer,

e.g. 'Ebenezer who?' 'Ebenezer black wood'
    'Eulalia who?' 'Eulalia nate my affections'
    'Cecilia who?' 'Cecilia game than I thought'

Across

1 *'Blank who?' 'Blank sitting down a minute?'*

7 *'Blank who?' 'Blank 'd love to'.*

Down

1 ⎫ *'Blank who?' 'Blank a*
9 ⎭ *wireless?'*

2 reversed. Brownsea Island is in this harbour.

Across

11 The sum I do here has chemical results (6).

12 They have ends, but they're really beginnings – twelve a year (7).

13 Summary way of making a cab start (8).

14 Stop! – or proceed slowly if the road is (5).

15 To make these you begin with leaves, and end with roots – even if they end in smoke (8).

19 Is it his unnatural need and baffled rage which makes him so false, the rat? (8).

22 Men go like this, little man (5).

24 Truly rural, he is, though not till he's had his beer! (8).

27 It takes two on 'em to do it properly (7).

28 Not experienced, so if you haven't got the right 'un try the left 'un (6).

29 It's dear and old when you sing about it, but it sings for the camper when it's new and cheap (5).

30 Hides away, but shows that the island lies between the South and South-east (8).

31 You may safely do so to the baby; otherwise you might get landed! (6).

32 Lots and lots, though they may be reduced to a shred (5).

Down

5 There's a hindrance en route, and that makes the game merely one of chance (8).

6 It really is a moving spectacle to see Mother after the cows!

7 'Tear asunder a broken reed' is one account of it, but it's another kind of account which usually is (8).

8 A design which is revealed in the name of the Law (6).

10 An untidy study is naturally bound to be (5).

16 She doesn't sound as if she were mass-produced, so she should render good service (8).

17 Considerably abashed, as Vera would be by a proposal like this! (8).

18 To get across, let art go one way and poetry the other (8).

20 You can't approve his way of getting money, especially as he's got enough under his head to keep a roof over his head (7).

21 Foxes had them long before the wireless was thought of (6).

22 This is desire in an immoderate degree, so the degree should be modified and diminished (5).

23 Spoil a good drink? Why, it's the outside edge! (6).

25 Pitch and toss. If you're right in this you won't be left in this (5).

26 They make an end of themselves, being mere creatures of fancy (5).

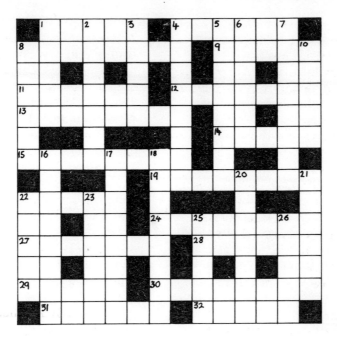

243. A Crossword by Ximenes ☆☆☆☆

Ximenes, whose real name was Derrick Somerset MacNutt, was the successor of Torquemada in the *Observer*, and was probably the greatest crossword compiler of all time. Here is one of his difficult puzzles.

Across

1 Dam chilly in Scotland (5).
5 Rush needed here – it could be prussic (7).
11 This fruit will be nearly made into jelly if you turn the gas out (10).
12 Audibly masticate a pie and thin cake (8).
14 In black I win – more often than not (4).
15 Almost a stink about a cap that's red (7).
16 Sat working with hardened felon in prison (6).

Down

1 Strutter, and what he isn't, seen at a fair (7).
2 Pitch with a hole, spoilt – I was cautious (10).
3 Bits of lava envelop unfortunate one (7).
4 Tipple before a series of excitements (5).
6 Irish tenant has a small boat and a row (7).
7 Antelope occupying a den got up (6).
8 Pages and pages make a big bore – skim (4).

Across

18 See where a river runs with broad branches (5).

19 Old Soldier afire in anticipation (7).

24 Car tire has become unpredictable (7).

25 I'm rapid: if unfinished, I show impatience (5).

26 Yearly split – so will one shock the kids? (6)

28 About to sprout: those that don't will die (7).

30 It's an advantage to move like a crab (4).

31 Indian farmer in daze, mind arrested (8).

32 Film presentations, big bits to be scrapped (10).

33 Modern poet seems to be extravagant (7).

34 Rude men, baffled by aitches (5).

Down

9 Salt, a small portion found in feathers (8).

10 Lester's first in a race – no longer rare (5).

13 Tiny nail to cut into a pendulous tree (10).

17 A soft sheen in a sheaf of volutes (8).

20 Pains once taken about sin of the world (7).

21 Rout of German – nought; should be Austrian (7).

22 Nasty disease – its cure is complicated (7).

23 Jammed and stuck about right-hand side (6).

25 Confront angry mongrel (5).

27 In flight – it's terrible (5).

29 What Jock hoes, upwards – its edge is sharp (4).

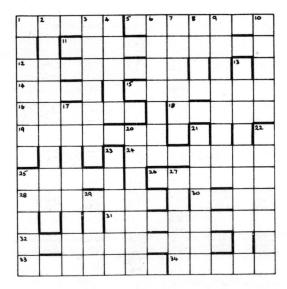

244. Contrary Crossword ☆☆☆

The answers are words opposite in meanings to the clues. For example if
the clue is FINISH the answer might be START or BEGIN.

Also, the answers are inserted not from left to right (ACROSS) and
from top to bottom (DOWN) as in a normal crossword, but from right to
left (BACK) and from bottom to top (UP).

BACK

1   Affluent (5).
2   Helps (7).
3   Figurative (7).
4   Adorned (5).
6   Takes (5).
8   Concentrated (7).
12 Worked (6).
14 Multiply (6).
15 Health (7).
16 Sour (5).
17 Equatorial (5).
18 Success (7).
22 Lax (7).
25 Sluggish (5).

UP

5   Prose (5).
7   Relaxed (5).
8   Shallowness (5).
9   Children (6).
10 Conceal (7).
11 Darken (7).
13 Hero (7).
19 Commons (5).
20 Truly (7).
21 Attract (5).
22 Debit (6).
23 Believed (7).
24 Humility (5).
25 Accepted (7).

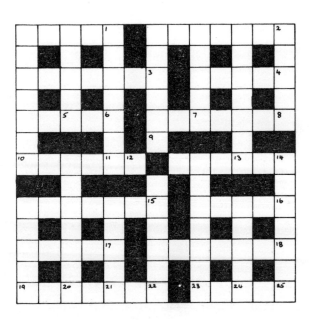

245. An Anagram Crossword ☆☆☆

This puzzle is by Michael Curl, who creates crosswords for a number of British newspapers and magazines.

In this crossword the clues are simply anagrams.

Across
1 Centaurs.
5 Rested.
9 Sceptres.
10 Recipe.
11 Shingled.
12 Strait.
14 Undressing.
18 Impression.
22 Dagger.
23 Salesmen.
24 Routed.
25 Presides.
26 Trance.
27 Gantries.

Down
1 Hearty.
2 Enters.
3 Tassel.
4 Stagnation.
6 Resisted.
7 Engrains.
8 Treaties.
13 Coordinate.
15 Picadors.
16 Berthing.
17 Insecure.
19 Peered.
20 Recede.
21 Stares.

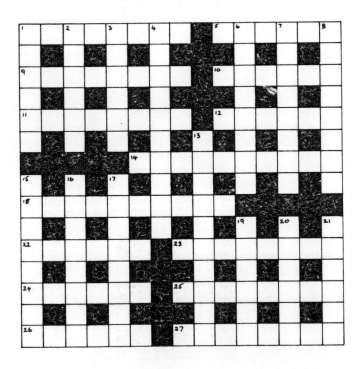

246. Two Miniature Crosswords ☆☆☆

These two crosswords by Michael Curl are small but perfectly formed.

(a)

Across
1 Greek horseman.
5 Some epic adored by a bullfighter.
6 Dante is translated in lieu.
7 Confused as sleep slips away.

Down
1 Overturn? It's a measure of one's bigheadedness!
2 A coin is collected as capital.
3 A speech – and where it should be delivered?
4 Sort of red rose found in church.

(b)

Across
1 House in open land?
5 Actor – one appearing in musical.
6 Asian queen in New Spain.
7 Reunite, somehow, in a train.

Down
1 Fall from a harvester?
2 Ragtime composition for a sleuth.
3 If you want a personal view, there's nothing to a cogwheel.
4 It's unusual for a saint to wander.

247. A Crossword by Luzzatto ☆☆☆

The modern American crossword has evolved in quite a different way from its British counterpart. Here is an example by Jack Luzzatto, one of the most popular crossword compilers in America.

Across

1 Criticize for error.
6 —— kebab.
11 Epoch.
14 Steel shielding.
15 Made a bridge of boats to cross a river.
17 White oak of California.
18 A time between.
19 Eggs with imagination.
21 Hurts and disables.
22 Hindu dress.
23 Quiet periods.
25 Overrule.
27 Magician's word.
29 Icy pinnacle amid a crevasse.
30 Hot dry desert wind.
33 Boola-boola university.
35 Superb craftsmanship.
36 Device to change function.
38 Dining alcove.
40 Central: Abbr.
41 Waterless.
43 Wooded area.
44 Fine threads.
46 Categories of plants or animals.
48 Letter A, in communications.
49 A well-planned crime.
50 Heroic tale.
54 Submarine detector.
56 Spaces for stowing cargo.
58 Of atomic particles.
60 Shame.
61 Weaken the foundation.
62 Chosen few.
63 Manuscripts: Abbr.
64 Waned.
65 Consonants said softly.

Down

1 Western card game.
2 Cooking fragrance.
3 Brown oil paint.
4 Sop for a tot.
5 Coatrack.
6 Damages out of malice.
7 Integrity.
8 Bank dividend: Abbr.
9 Stanches.
10 Israeli dance.
11 Count each one.
12 Colorful warblers.
13 Soft drink.
16 Martini additive.
20 Slight quake.
24 Sycophant.
26 Group of eight.
28 Rolls of names, for duty.
29 Spanish title.
30 —— Guitry, French actor.
31 Boy paragons: 2 wds.
32 Makes many copies.
34 Long-term convicts.
37 Latvian seaport capital.
39 Delible.
42 Step out onto the landing strip.
45 Rajah's wife.
47 Approached.
49 Morse
51 Repeatedly.
52 Beau ——.
53 Partner of sackcloth.
55 Land measure.
57 Chinese money of account.
58 Not talking.
59 Movement for freedom, for short.

248. Another Crossword by Luzzatto ☆☆☆

Here is another crossword by Jack Luzzatto.

Across

1 Drank.
8 Intimidator.
14 Experience.
15 Poison gas from antimony.
16 Wins affection.
17 Four-element vacuum tube.
18 Former Brazilian money.
19 Breakout.
21 Flee.
22 U.S. tax service.
23 Ship ends.

Down

1 Questioned to clear up doubt.
2 Rattle.
3 Steele's literary partner.
4 Professional charges.
5 Monk's title.
6 Fine-plumed heron.
7 Bedded down in a flophouse.
8 Paces.
9 Mention.
10 Hebrew patriarch: Abbr.
11 Broadway girl of the past.

Across

24 Encircled.
25 Summon forth.
27 Acted so.
28 Dwindle.
29 Abnegation.
31 Martial.
33 Lack of originality.
35 Frill or ruffle.
38 Mental lethargy.
42 Tale of a classic siege.
43 Used to be.
45 Think so.
46 Ladder step.
47 Mine disaster.
49 Run the engine.

Down

12 Sufferer.
13 Return to earth.
15 Substitute actor.
20 Lots of trouble for the police.
23 Scorched.
24 Arises.
26 Handy travel sack.
28 Valve in a wind instrument.
30 Mae West role.
32 French plural article.
34 Haulable by rope.
35 Andiron.
36 Howl weirdly.
37 Skater.
39 Bayou canoe.

Across
50 Large deer.
51 Threads for cloth.
52 Sun hat.
53 Doggone stupid.
55 Outside the law.
57 Of the eared seals.
58 Main movie on program.
59 Slaves of the lamp.
60 City roads.

Down
40 Single installment in a magazine: 2 wds.
41 Heaps abuse upon.
44 Strokes on typefaces.
47 Twigs or shoots for grafting.
48 Small island.
51 Pâté de —— gras.
52 Head: Fr.
54 Last workday for most: Abbr.
56 Household god.

249. Cryptic Acrostic 1 ☆☆☆

Solve the clues and place the answers into one of the two smaller grids next to their clue letters. Then transfer the letters of the answers to their matching numbered squares in the large grid where a quotation will appear.

The initial letters of the answers will spell out the title of the book, and its author, from which the quotation was taken.

A. It's worth starting up in the valley
B. Concentrating under canvas?
C. Terribly loud game
D. Do nothing to produce bread
E. Electrical connection between Mars and Venus?
F. River seen on golf-course?
G. Edward's little cuddly toy
H. Eastern agreement for viewers
J. Young animal with an islander
K. Do they entertain armies?
L. The man composing a song
M. Maigret's sort of music?
N. West gets taken outside, being obscene
P. Part of the body that produces music?
Q. Object seen when night falls?
R. Faith is tied up, so we hear
S. Engrave some sketches
T. Short of fibre
U. Reckless skin complaint
V. Beginning with the exterior group?
W. Almost night? Almost!
X. The short measure is a crime!
Y. Anaesthetic could be there

A	51	23	98	9	100	
B	95	45	38	3	81	17
C	78	93	112	57		
D	12	108	33	74		
E	21	48	65	1	104	
F	87	36	71	6		
G	19	61	107	82	69	
H	99	106	5	41		
J	29	85	53	64	101	
K	2	111	90	59	14	
L	27	96	66	18	52	67

M	84	31	10	103	16	73	40
N	28	79	15	102			
P	110	43	11	68	22		
Q	24	98	50	55	109		
R	49	8	25	91	76		
S	13	97	34	60			
T	92	37	77	63	83		
U	26	80	4	62			
V	44	75	56	70	89	35	
W	47	86	46	30			
X	94	39	54	58	7		
Y	105	42	20	72	32		

1E	2K	3B	4U	5H		6F	7X	8R	9A	10M	11P	12D	13S
14K		15N	16M	17B	18L		19G	20Y	21E		22P	23A	24Q
25R	26U	27L	28N		29J	30W	31M	32Y	33D	34S	35V	36F	37T
	38B	39X	40M		41H	42Y	43P	44V	45B	46W		47W	48E
49R	50Q	51A	52L		53J	54X	55Q	56V		57C	58X		59K
60S	61G		62U	63T	64J	65E	66L		67L	68P	69G		70V
71F	72Y	73M		74D	75V	76R	77T	78C	79N		80U	81B	82G
	83T	84M	85J	86W	87F	88A	89V	90K	91R		92T	93C	94X
	95B	96L		97S	98Q	99H		100A	101J	102N		103M	104E
105Y	106H		107G	108D		109Q	110P	111K	112C				

250. Cryptic Acrostic 2 ☆☆☆

Solve the clues and place the answers into one of the two smaller grids next to their clue letters. Then transfer the letters of the answers to their matching numbered squares in the large grid where a quotation will appear.

A	9	127	32	106	87	51	72	
B	100	55	28	109	70	58	42	
C	126	8	63	25	57	105	41	92
D	82	65	103	97	77	69	43	
E	107	35	50	128	108	90		
F	49	2	38	24	34	104	68	
G	118	40	71	125	20	91	27	
H	31	6	59	21	124	1	86	119
J	74	132	67	96	85	16	56	
K	22	88	120	79	12	46	5	
L	84	29	61	122	99			
M	23	102	7	53	80	33		
N	45	95	116	66	4	39		
P	115	44	52	36	121	15	10	83
Q	94	11	13	48	130	64		
R	54	101	30	81	117	98		
S	89	47	131	76				
T	37	123	14	110	60	111	75	
U	114	73	113	3	26	18		
V	112	62	78	93	17	129	19	

The initial letters of the answers will spell out the title of the book, and its author, from which the quotation was taken.

A. Turner is a cheat! (7)
B. A fish had a weed (7)
C. Charm one's way in (8)
D. Several new shows! (7)
E. Making a request like a ruler (6)
F. He does not believe in Castro (7)
G. Now present – but not in any place (7)
H. But rings may be splitting (8)
J. Rhetoric – or standing beside a politician (7)
K. Lash pet dog (7)
L. Study, perhaps, requiring a sweep? (5)
M. Basket that may be an impediment? (6)
N. Learner, terrible but legal (6)
P. Sailors in the drink (8)
Q. Break the law to obtain riches (6)
R. Royal Engineers have two to mend (6)
S. Employ sound sheep (4)
T. Ron goes back to people in the county (7)
U. Chicken or cow on a road (6)
V. Observing eastern espionage (7)

1H	2F		3U	4N	5K	6H	7M	8C		9A	10P	11Q		12K	13Q
14T	15P	16J	17V	18U	19V	20G	21H		22K	23M	24F	25C	26U	27G	28B
	29L	30R		31H	32A	33M	34F	35E		36P	37T		38F	39N	40G
41C	42B	43D		44P	45N	46K	47S		48Q	49F	50E	51A		52P	53M
54R	55B	56J		57C	58B	59H	60T	61L	62V		63C	64Q	65D		66N
67J	68F	69D	70B	71G		72A	73U	74J	75T	76S		77D	78V	79K	80M
81R	82D	83P	84L		85J	86H		87A	88K	89S		90E	91G	92C	93V
	94Q	95N	96J	97D	98R	99L		100B	101R	102M	103D	104F	105C	106A
107E	108E	109B		110T	111T	112V	113U		114U	115P	116N	117R	118G	119H
120K	121P	122L	123T		124H	125G	126C		127A	128E	129V	130Q	131S	132J

251. Spiralword ☆☆☆

The answers are to be entered spirally into the diagram, the last two or
more letters of each answer forming the beginning of the next one.

1 Unassuming.
2 Warship.
3 Fur.
4 Planet.
5 Notwithstanding.
6 Absolutely necessary.
7 Height.
8 Flood.
9 Japanese entertainer.
10 Disadvantage.
11 Competent.
12 Young hare.
13 Game dog.
14 Word for word.
15 Huge.
16 Signalling system.
17 American state.

18 Burdensome.
19 Person seizing power.
20 Ground that's always frozen.
21 Salary.
22 Strive.
23 Suave.
24 The drink of the gods.
25 Craftsman.
26 Firedog.
27 Wild ass.
28 Scholarly.
29 Storm.
30 Dagger.
31 Poison.
32 Blue dye.
33 Giant champion of the
   Philistines.

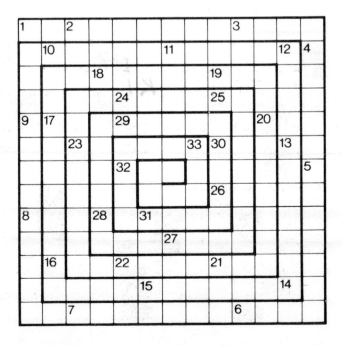

252. Codeword ☆☆☆

In this crossword each letter of the alphabet is represented by a number. The problem is to work out which letter each number represents. We have given you three letters to start you off. If you fill in these letters wherever the corresponding number occurs in the diagram, it should not take you too long to determine the other letters.

10. QUICK THINKING

253. ✩✩

Which number gives the same result when it is divided by −6 as when it is subtracted from −6?

254. ✩✩

Which three numbers give the same result when they are added as when they are multiplied together.

255. ✩

There are five apples in a basket and five people in a room. How can you give an apple to each person and still leave an apple in the basket?

256. ✩✩✩

The number 1729 is the smallest number that may be expressed as the sum of two cubes in two different ways. What are the two ways?

257. ✩✩

Which are there more of: inches in a mile or Sundays in a thousand years?

258. ✩✩

Which are there more of: seconds in a week or feet in 100 miles?

259. ✩✩

Which is heavier: 1000 kilograms or 1 ton?

260. ✩✩

Which is longer: 250 centimetres or 8 feet?

261. ✩✩

Which is colder: minus 40 degrees Centigrade or minus 40 degrees Fahrenheit?

262. ☆☆

Which is longer:
- (a) 666 days or 95 weeks?
- (b) 666 inches or 55 feet?
- (c) 666 hours or 28 days?
- (d) 666 millimetres or 2 feet?
- (e) 666 minutes or one-fourteenth of a week?

263. ☆☆

A driver goes once round a 5-mile circular track at 30 miles per hour. How fast must he travel on the second lap in order to average 60 miles per hour for the two laps?

264. ☆☆

What is the value of one-half of two-thirds of three-quarters of four-fifths of five-sixths of six-sevenths of seven-eighths of eight-ninths of nine-tenths of 1000?

265. ☆☆

In a race, the runner who came three places in front of the runner who finished last came two places ahead of the runner who came seventh.
　　How many finished the race?

266. ☆☆

A man smoked 100 cigarettes in five days, each day smoking six more than on the previous day.
　　How many cigarettes did he smoke on the first day?

267. ☆☆

If you put a coin into an empty bottle and then insert a cork into the neck of the bottle, how can you get the coin out of the bottle without taking out the cork or breaking the bottle?

268. ☆☆

A man had a square swimming pool in his garden with a tree growing at each corner, like this:

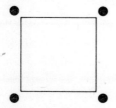

How could he double the size of his swimming pool, keeping it square, without cutting down or moving any of the trees?

269. ☆☆

Can you draw four straight lines through these nine dots without lifting your pen from the paper?

● ● ●

● ● ●

● ● ●

270. ☆☆

If I said to you 'I will bet you £1 that if you gave me £2 I will give you £3 in return' would that be a good bet for you to accept?

271. ☆☆

A's watch is 5 minutes fast but he thinks it is 10 minutes slow. B's watch is 10 minutes slow but he thinks it is 5 minutes fast. They both plan to catch the 12 o'clock train. Who gets to the station first?

272. ☆☆

A boy has as many sisters as brothers, but each sister has only half as many sisters as brothers.
    How many boys and how many girls are there in the family?

273. ☆☆

How many triangles are there in this diagram?

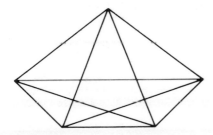

274. ☆☆

I am thinking of a three-digit number. If you subtract 8 from it, the result is divisible by 8. If you add 9 to it, the result is divisible by 9. If you subtract 7 from it, the result is divisible by 7. What is the number?

275. ☆☆☆

What is the sum of all the integers from 1 to 2000?

276. ☆☆☆

How many times on average must an ordinary six-sided die be tossed before every number from one to six comes up at least once?

277. ☆☆

A traveller in a strange country, with no map, comes to a crossroads where a signpost has been knocked down. How can he find his way without asking anyone for directions?

278. ☆☆☆

If twenty people, on parting, all shake hands with each other once, how many handshakes will there be altogether?

279. ☆☆

Show how six sixes can equal a gross.

280. ☆☆

Can you think of common English words containing:
    (a) two double E's?
    (b) two double O's?
    (c) two double S's?
    (d) two double F's?

281. ☆☆☆

Can you think of common English words of 9 letters containing:
    (a) five E's?
    (b) five S's?

11. MODERN MASTERS

HUBERT PHILLIPS

Hubert Phillips has had thousands of puzzles published both under his own name and his pseudonym of 'Caliban' – in publications such as the *Daily Telegraph*, the *Evening Standard*, the *New Statesman*, the *Law Journal* and countless others.

282. Good Eggs ☆☆☆☆

'You don't like arithmetic, child?' said Humpty Dumpty. 'I don't very much.'

'But I thought you were good at sums,' said Alice.

'So I am,' said Humpty Dumpty. 'Good at sums; oh, certainly. But what has that to do with liking them? When I qualified as a Good Egg – many, many years ago, that was – I got a better mark in arithmetic than any of the others who qualified. Not that that's saying a lot. None of us did as well in arithmetic as in any other subject.'

'How many subjects were there?' said Alice, interested.

'Ah!' said Humpty Dumpty, 'I must think. The number of subjects was one-third of the number of marks obtainable in any one subject. And I ought to mention that in no two subjects did I get the same mark, and that is also true of the other Good Eggs who qualified.'

'But you haven't told me —' began Alice.

'I know I haven't,' said Humpty Dumpty. 'I haven't told you how many marks in all one had to obtain to qualify. Well, I'll tell you now. It was a number equal to four times the maximum obtainable in one subject. And we all just managed to qualify.'

'But how many —' said Alice.

'I'm coming to that,' said Humpty Dumpty. 'How many of us were there? Well, when I tell you that no two of us obtained the same assortment of marks – a thing which was only just possible – you'll be well on the way to the answer. But to make it as easy as I can for you, I'll put it another way. The number of other Good Eggs who qualified when I did, multiplied by the number of subjects (I've told you about that already), gives a product equal to half the total number of marks obtained by each Good Egg. And now you can find out all you want to know.' He composed himself for a nap.

Alice was almost in tears. 'I can't,' she said, 'do any of it. Isn't it differential equations, or something I've never learned?'

Humpty Dumpty opened one eye. 'Don't be a fool, child,' he said crossly. 'Anyone ought to be able to do it, who is able to count on five fingers.'

What was Humpty Dumpty's mark in arithmetic?

283. Helpuselph ☆☆☆

A settler in the island of Helpuselph applied to the Governor for some land. 'How much would you like?' asked the Governor.

'About 100 square miles.'

'Okay,' said the Governor. 'You may choose a rectangular parcel of land in the township of Little Rainfall. Its dimensions must be such that, if one side of the rectangle were 5 miles longer, and the other 4 miles longer, the area of the rectangle would be twice as great; and its perimeter must be exactly 46 miles.'

The applicant duly selected and fenced his land in accordance with these conditions. But he got away with six square miles more than the Governor had anticipated.

What was the area of the selected rectangle?

284. Dodecahedra ☆☆☆☆

I have an indefinite number of regular dodecahedra, indistinguishable in appearance from one another. I have pots of red and blue paint. If each face of each dodecahedron is to be painted red or blue, how many dodecahedra which are distinguishable from one another shall I be able to produce?

DAVID WELLS

Here are three puzzles from David Wells, professional puzzler and games inventor, and former editor of the magazine *Games and Puzzles*.

285. Behind the Scenes ☆☆☆

The results were about to be announced in the annual Ruritanian song festival, but there was apparently some delay. Gradually the word was passed round that one of the four finalists, instead of giving three marks to the other finalist he rated highest, and two marks for the next best finalist and one mark for the third best (naturally no finalist was asked to rate his own song), had reversed the marks given, hoping to improve his own chances. He had given one mark to his best choice, two marks to his middle choice and three marks to the finalist he actually thought worst.

The commotion was of course tremendous and it only increased when it was revealed that two of the other finalists had taken exactly the same dishonest step in the hope, so they thought, of improving *their* chances.

Before these revelations were made all four finalists had been tied on six points. When the judges eventually reversed the marking orders of the three dishonest finalists, in what place did the honest singer find himself?

286. Electronic Lullaby ☆☆

Our small neighbour was given an electronics set for Christmas and we have had no peace since. His latest model is an electronic organ. Unfortunately, it only plays three notes: a high note, *ping*, a middle note, *mmmmmm*, and a low note, *boing*. He has wired these up so that the same note repeated, for example *ping-ping*, is immediately followed by an *mmmmmm*. A note followed by a lower note is followed in turn by *ping*, and a note following a lower note is then followed by a *boing*.

Really quite impressive for a twelve-year-old, but the contraption is getting on our nerves. Can you explain why?

287. Trigger Happy ☆☆☆

'So how much do we know?' asked Patterson, doodling with his pencil on the desk.

'It's a five-figure number and it's a perfect square,' replied Gerson, 'but don't forget that if we get the wrong number the mechanism will jam and we'll lose all chance of detonating it.' He drummed his fingers. The phone rang. He picked it up.

'Good heavens! Yes!' He looked at Patterson. 'The first two figures are 69, and it reads the same either way! That must fix it, surely? The number is palindromic.' Patterson scribbled quickly on his pad. '26 . . . 265 . . . 264, ah, 264 squared is 69696, just a moment . . . mmmm, that's it.' He looked up at Gerson and grinned. Gerson picked up the phone and spoke quickly, then sat back and said nothing. After several minutes, the phone rang again and he picked it up confidently . 'Yes? It's . . . jammed?' Beads of sweat appeared on his forehead and Patterson felt sick. What had gone wrong?

PIERRE BERLOQUIN

The puzzles of Pierre Berloquin are tremendously popular in his native France. He has published several books of puzzles, as well as many other books about indoor games, and has regular columns in the magazine *Science et Vie* and in the Paris newspaper *Le Monde*. Here are two puzzles selected from his works.

288. Cross-Country ☆☆☆

Every month Timothy, Urban and Vincent run cross-country before breakfast.

After a month they realize that Timothy has finished before Urban more often than after him and that Urban has finished before Vincent more often than after him.

Is it possible that Vincent has finished before Timothy more often than after him?

289. Five Friends ☆☆☆

Five friends, Andrew, Bernard, Claude, Donald and Eugene, each have a son and a daughter. Their families are so close that each has married his daughter to the son of one of his friends, and as a result the daughter-in-law of the father of Andrew's son-in-law is the sister-in-law of Bernard's son, and the son-in-law of the father of Claude's daughter-in-law is the brother-in-law of Donald's daughter.

But although the daughter-in-law of the father of Bernard's daughter-in-law has the same mother-in-law as the son-in-law of the father of Donald's son-in-law, the situation is simplified by the fact that no daughter-in-law is the sister-in-law of the daughter of her father-in-law.

Who married Eugene's daughter?

BORIS KORDEMSKY

Boris Kordemsky, who was born in 1907, is a retired secondary school mathematics teacher living in Moscow. He has produced several books on mathematics and on mathematical recreations. But it is for his collection of puzzles, *Mathematical Know-how*, first published in 1956, that he is famous. This work has been translated from the original Russian into Ukrainian, Estonian, Lettish and Lithuanian. Outside the USSR translations of the book have appeared in Bulgaria, Hungary, Rumania, Poland, Czechoslovakia, France, Germany, China, Japan and Korea. The following four puzzles are taken from this collection.

290. Down and Up ☆☆☆

A boy presses a side of a blue pencil to a side of a yellow pencil, holding both pencils vertically. One inch of the pressed side of the blue pencil, measuring from its lower end, is smeared with paint. The yellow pencil is held steady while the boy slides the blue pencil down 1 inch, continuing to press it against the yellow one. He returns the blue pencil to its former position, then slides it down 1 inch. He continues until he has lowered the blue pencil 5 times and raised it 5 times – 10 moves in all.

Suppose that during this time the paint neither dries nor diminishes in quantity. How many inches of each pencil will be smeared with paint after the tenth move?

This problem was thought up by the mathematician Leonid Mikhailovitch Rybakov while on his way home after a successful duck hunt. What led him to make up this puzzle is explained in the answer, but don't read it until you have solved the problem.

291. Large Segments Instead of Small ☆☆☆

In the Soviet machine industry a marker is a man who draws lines on a metal blank. The blank is cut along the lines to produce the desired shape.

A marker was asked to distribute 7 equal-sized sheets of metal among 12 workers, each worker to get the same amount of metal. He could not use the simple solution of dividing each sheet into 12 equal parts, for this would result in too many tiny pieces. What was he to do?

He thought awhile and found a more convenient method.

Later he easily divided 5 sheets for 6 workers, 13 for 12, 13 for 36, 26 for 21, and so on.

What was his method?

292. A Jar with Lead Shot ☆☆

The builders of an irrigation canal needed a lead plate of a certain size, but had no lead in stock. They decided to melt some lead shot. But how could they find its volume beforehand?

One suggestion was to measure a ball, apply the formula for the volume of a sphere, and multiply by the number of balls. But this would take too long, and anyway the shot wasn't all the same size.

Another was to weigh all the shot and divide by the specific gravity of lead. Unfortunately, no one could remember this ratio, and there was no manual in the field shop.

Another was to pour the shot into a gallon jug. But the volume of the jug is greater than the volume of the shot by an undetermined amount, since the shot cannot be packed solid and part of the jug contains air.

Do you have a suggestion?

293. A Singular Trip ☆☆☆☆

Two boys go on a bicycle trip. En route one of the bicycles breaks down and has to be left behind for repairs. They decide to share the remaining bicycle. They start simultaneously, one on bicycle, one on foot. At a certain point the cyclist dismounts, leaves the bicycle behind, and continues on foot. His friend, when he reaches the waiting bicycle, mounts it and rides until he catches up with his friend, who takes the bicycle, and so on.

How far from their destination should the bicycle be left behind the last time so they reach the destination simultaneously? The distance from breakdown to destination is 60 miles, and they each walk 5 miles per hour and bicycle 15 miles per hour.

MARTIN GARDNER

Martin Gardner, born 1914, is well known for his recreational mathematics columns in *Scientific American*, which ran for over two decades, and for the numerous collections of puzzles and mathematical diversions that he has had published. Here are three examples.

294. The Circle on the Chessboard ☆☆☆

A chess board has squares that are two inches on the side. What is the radius of the largest circle that can be drawn on the board in such a way that the circle's circumference is entirely on black squares?

295. Dividing the Cake ☆☆☆

There is a simple procedure by which two people can divide a cake so that each is satisfied he has at least half: One cuts and the other chooses. Devise a general procedure so that n persons can cut a cake into n portions in such a way that everyone is satisfied he has at least 1/n of the cake.

296. Three Prisoners ☆☆☆

Three men – A, B and C – were in separate cells under sentence of death when the state governor decided to pardon one of them. He wrote their names on three slips of paper, shook the slips in a hat, drew out one of them, and telephoned the prisoner governor, requesting that the name of the lucky man be kept secret for several days. Rumour of this reached prisoner A. When the governor made his morning rounds, A tried to persuade the governor to tell him who had been pardoned. The governor refused.

'Then tell me,' said A, 'the name of one of the others who will be executed. If B is to be pardoned, give me C's name. If C is to be pardoned, give me B's name. And if I'm to be pardoned, toss a coin to decide whether to name B or C.'

'But if you see me toss the coin,' replied the wary governor, 'you'll know that you're the one pardoned. And if you see that I don't toss a coin, you'll know it's either you or the person I don't name.'

'Then don't tell me now,' said A. 'Tell me tomorrow morning.'

The governor, who knew nothing about probability theory, thought it over that night and decided that if he followed the procedure suggested by A, it would give A no help whatever in estimating his survival chances. So next morning he told A that B was going to be executed.

After the governor left, A smiled to himself at the governor's stupidity. There were now only two equally probable elements in what mathematicians like to call the 'sample space' of the problem. Either C would be pardoned or himself, so by all the laws of conditional probability, his chances of survival had gone up from 1/3 to 1/2.

The governor did not know that A could communicate with C, in an adjacent cell, by tapping in code on a water pipe. This A proceeded to do, explaining to C exactly what he had said to the governor and what the governor had said to him. C was equally overjoyed with the news because he figures, by the same reasoning used by A, that his own survival chances had also risen to 1/2.

Did the two men reason correctly? If not, how should each have calculated his chances of being pardoned?

DAVID SILVERMAN

David Silverman, a resident of Los Angeles, established his reputation on the basis of one incredible book called *Your Move* as a brilliant creator of original puzzles. The following three puzzles are taken from that book.

297. The Truel ☆☆☆☆

After a mutual and irreconcilable dispute among Red, Black and Blue, the three parties have agreed to a three-way duel. Each man is provided a pistol and an unlimited supply of ammunition. Instead of simultaneous volleys, a firing order is to be established and followed until only one survivor remains.

Blue is a 100 per cent marksman, never having missed a bull's-eye in his shooting career. Black is successful two out of three times on the average, and you, Red, are only a 1/3 marksman. Recognizing the disparate degrees of marksmanship, the seconds have decided that you will be the first and Black second in the firing order.

Your pistol is loaded and cocked. At whom do you fire?

298. Yes or No? ☆☆☆

This is a variation of the game *Twenty Questions*, with a bit of *What's My Line?* thrown in to make it more interesting.

Red and Black each covertly write down an integer from 1 to 100. The objective is to guess the other player's number first. Questions may be asked concerning the opponent's number provided that they can be answered truthfully with a 'yes' or 'no'. A player is permitted to continue asking questions so long as he receives 'yes' answers. 'The first 'no' transfers the role of questioner to the opponent.

The conservative *Twenty Questions* strategy of questioning in such a manner as most nearly to equalise the chance of 'yes' and 'no' answers is most effective in that game. Using it, you can, in only twenty questions, invariably pinpoint any number in the range of 1 to 500,000. But in the game *Yes or No?* this may not be the best way to proceed.

Suppose you are the first player. What will your questioning strategy be, and how much of an advantage do you feel you have over your opponent?

299. Modified Russian Roulette ☆☆☆☆

In this harmless version of Russian Roulette, two players alternately shoot a six-shot revolver, only one chamber of which contains a cartridge, at a target. The player who first gets a 'bang' rather than a 'click' is the loser.

There is an option, however. At any turn, instead of shooting the next chamber, a player may randomly spin the magazine before shooting. Once either player elects to spin before shooting, all successive shots, if any, must be preceded by a spin.

You have first shot. Do you spin first and shoot, or shoot without spinning?

After you have worked this one out, decided what you would do as the first player in the *misère* version (first player to get a 'bang' wins).

12. TOMORROW'S CLASSICS

RUBIK'S CUBE

Rubik's Cube was a major world-wide sensation in 1980–1. Although the craze has now abated, the cube still continues to generate interest. It is used by teachers of mathematics as a teaching aid when dealing with group theory and the mathematics of symmetry. It has been given a permanent place in the New York Museum of Modern Art. But more importantly, as far as we are concerned, it continues to be the basis for new puzzles.

The three puzzles included here all involve producing a pattern from a 'plain' cube – that is, you start with a cube on which all nine squares on each face are similarly coloured.

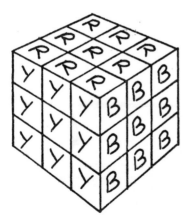

(In the diagram, the faces you can see are yellow, blue and red; the faces you cannot see are green, white and orange. It may be that the cube you use for these puzzles has a different colour arrangement – don't worry, the patterns produced will be the same even if the colours vary).

300. Cross-Check ☆☆☆

Starting with a plain cube, find the moves necessary to produce a cross-check pattern on all the six faces, as shown in the diagram.

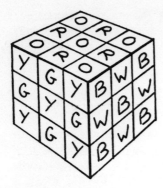

301. Stripes ✭✭✩

Starting with a plain cube, find the moves necessary to produce a stripe on four of the faces, as shown in the diagram.

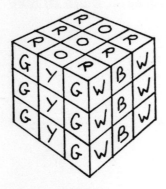

302. Dots ✭✭✭✩

Starting with a plain cube, find the moves necessary to produce a pattern like that shown, in which each of the six faces has a central 'spot' of a different colour from the rest of the face.

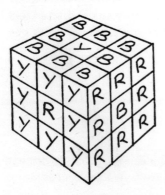

POCKET CALCULATOR PUZZLES

303. A Common Factor ☆☆☆

Perform these calculations:

$$8 \times 473 =$$
$$9 \times 351 =$$
$$15 \times 93 =$$
$$21 \times 87 =$$
$$27 \times 81 =$$
$$35 \times 41 =$$

What is the common factor?

304. Another Common Factor ☆☆☆

Perform these calculations:

$$483 \times 12 =$$
$$297 \times 18 =$$
$$198 \times 27 =$$
$$186 \times 39 =$$
$$138 \times 42 =$$
$$154 \times 48 =$$

What is the common factor?

305. Hidden Significance ☆☆

Perform the following calculations on your calculator. Each answer has some literal significance. If you don't see it at first, try looking at the answer from a different perspective.

(a) $(366 \times 10) + (4 \times 11)$
(b) $(366 \times 15) + (4 \times 55)$
(c) $(366 \times 16) - (3 \times 41)$
(d) $(366 \times 19) + (3 \times 17) + 100$
(e) $(366 \times 20) + (9 \times 44)$
(f) $(366 \times 21) + (4 \times 37)$
(g) $(366 \times 2) + 230^2 + 119$
(h) $(366 \times 867) + (5 \times 43)$

SCIENCE FICTION AND SCIENCE FACT

The next two puzzles are Science Fiction Puzzle Tales by Martin Gardner – but today's science fiction is tomorrow's science fact.

306. Tube Through the Earth ☆☆☆☆

In the twenty-third century an enormous gravity transport tube, with a diameter of 20 metres, was constructed straight along the earth's axis to join the metropolises of North Polaris and South Polaris. Through this tunnel cylindrical cars carrying both supplies and people were dropped from one city to the other. All friction was eliminated by maintaining a vacuum inside the tube, and by using magnetic fields to keep the cars away from the tube's side. The trip from pole to pole took only slightly longer than 42 minutes.

How many of the following questions about the transport tube can you answer?

(1) As the car travels from North Polaris to the earth's centre, does its velocity increase, decrease, or stay the same?

(2) Does the car's *acceleration* increase, decrease, or remain the same?

(3) If you are riding in a car and it stops halfway down to the earth's centre, would you weigh less or more on a spring scale than on the earth's surface?

(4) At what point during the trip would you experience zero gravity?

(5) At what spot does the car reach maximum speed, and how fast is it going?

(6) If a car fell down a similar tube through the centre of the moon, would the time for a one-way trip be shorter or longer than 42 minutes?

(7) A famous SF story was written about an attempt to dig a deep hole below the earth's crust. It turns out that the earth is a living organism, and when its epidermis is punctured the earth lets out a mighty yell of pain. What is the story's title and who wrote it?

307. Vacation on the Moon ☆☆☆☆

Edgar D. Twitchell, a New Jersey plumber, was on his way to the moon for a three-week holiday. The rocket ship was too small to generate artificial gravity by spinning, so Twitchell had the strange sensation of feeling his weight steadily diminish as the ship sped towards its destination. When it reached the spot where earth's stronger gravity field was exactly balanced by the moon's weaker field, zero g prevailed inside the ship. All passengers were kept fastened to their seats, but Twitchell enjoyed the floating feeling nonetheless as he twiddled his thumbs and contentedly puffed a cigar.

Many hours later the ship slowly settled next to one of the huge domes that house the US moon colony, its descent cushioned by rocket brakes. Through the thick glass window by his seat Twitchell caught his first glimpse of the spectacular lunar landscape. Several large seagulls, with tiny oxygen tanks strapped to their backs, were flying near the dome. Above the dome an American flag fluttered in the breeze.

Although it was daylight, the sky was inky black and splattered with twinkling stars. Low on the horizon a rising 'New Earth' showed a thin bluish crescent of light with several faint stars shining between the crescent's arms. As Twitchell later learned, the moon makes one rotation during each revolution around the earth. Because a rotation takes about twenty-eight days, it takes the earth about fourteen days to rise and set on the moon.

On the sixth day of his vacation, Twitchell was allowed to put on a space suit and hike around the crater in which the dome had been built. After bounding along for a while he came upon a group of children, in pink space suits, playing with boomerangs. One girl tossed a boomerang that made a wide circle and Twitchell had to duck as it whirled past his helmet. Behind him he heard it thud against a large boulder. He turned to look, but the curved stick had fallen into the rock's ebony shadow where it instantly seemed to vanish. Since there is no atmospheric scattering of light on the moon, objects cannot be seen in shadows without a flashlight.

The sun was low in the sky when Twitchell began his walk. Now it was sinking out of sight. The 'terminator', that sharp line separating the lunar day from night, was gliding across the gray terrain toward the brightly lit dome at a speed of about 40 miles an hour – much too fast for Twitchell to keep up with it by vigorous hopping. Overhead a meteor left a fiery trail as it fell to the moon's surface.

Twitchell was so exhausted when he returned to his quarters that he fell asleep on his bed, fully clothed, and did not awake until the rising sun flooded his room with brilliant sunlight.

How many scientific mistakes can you find in the above narrative?

COMPUTER-GENERATED PUZZLES

Perhaps the puzzles of the future will all be created (and solved?) by computers. Here, as a harbinger of things to come, are three puzzle-generating programs by Michael and David Curl, which are designed to be run on home micro-computers. Each of these programs generates puzzles of a particular format but, by using random variables, is able to produce a large number of different puzzles within that format. The programs will ask for your answers and will tell you whether you are right or wrong.

If you have a Spectrum computer, you can type in and run the programs just as they are shown here. If you own a different type of home computer, you will probably have to make one or two slight amendments to the programs before you can use them.

308. 'Age Puzzle' Program

```
10 RANDOMIZE
20 CLS
30 LET ted=5+INT (10*RND)
40 LET diff=2+INT (8*RND)
50 PRINT AT 3,10
60 PRINT TAB 10;"AGE PUZZLE"
70 PRINT AT 7,0
80 PRINT INK 3;" Dave is ";
90 PRINT INK 2;diff
100 PRINT INK 3;"years older than Ted"
110 PRINT AT 9,0
120 PRINT TAB 2;INK 3;"The sum of their age is ";
130 PRINT INK 2;diff+(2*ted)
140 PRINT AT 13,0
150 PRINT TAB 8;INK 3;"How old is Ted?"
160 INPUT TAB 12;INK 3;"Age??";INK 2;answer
170 IF answer=ted THEN GO TO 500
180 PRINT AT 17,10
190 PRINT INK 1;TAB 5;FLASH 1;" Sorry, that's wrong "
200 PRINT INK 1;TAB 5;FLASH 1;"The correct answer is "
210 PRINT INK 1;FLASH 1;ted;" "
220 PAUSE 300
230 GO TO 20
500 PRINT AT 17,10
510 PRINT TAB 5;INK 1;FLASH 1;" CORRECT! Well done! "
520 FOR n=1 to 5:BEEP .15,n:NEXT n
530 PAUSE 200
540 GO TO 20
```

309. 'Integer Product' Program

```
10 RANDOMIZE
20 CLS
30 LET x=5+INT (15*RND)
40 PRINT AT 4,0;INK 4;"xxxxxxxxxxxxxxxxxxxxxxxxxxxxxxxxxxx"
50 PRINT AT 4,7;INK 3;" PRODUCT PUZZLE "
60 PRINT AT 7,0
70 PRINT INK 1;" Three consecutive integers   are multiplied together"
80 PRINT AT 10,0
90 PRINT TAB 2;INK 2;"The product is ";
100 PRINT INK 2;x*(x+1)*(x+2)
110 PRINT AT 12,0
120 PRINT INK 1;" What is the lowest of the 3   integers?"
130 INPUT answer
140 IF answer=x THEN GO TO 500
150 PRINT AT 16,0
160 PRINT TAB 8;INK 3;FLASH 1;" You're wrong! "
170 PRINT AT 18,0
180 PRINT TAB 2;INK 3;FLASH 1; "The correct answer is "
190 PRINT INK 3;FLASH 1;x;" "
200 PAUSE 300
210 GO TO 20
500 PRINT AT 16,0
510 PRINT TAB 2;INK 3;FLASH 1;"Sure looks right to me! "
520 For n=-10 TO 30:BEEP .005,n:NEXT n
530 PAUSE 100
540 GO TO 20
```

310. 'Rectangle Puzzle' Program

```
10 RANDOMIZE
20 CLS
30 LET x=1+INT (10*RND)
40 LET y=x+1+INT (10*RND)
50 PRINT AT 3,7;
60 PRINT "RECTANGLE PUZZLE"
70 PRINT AT 7,0;
80 PRINT INK 1;"The perimeter of a rectangle is "
90 PRINT TAB 3;INK 3;2*(x+y)
100 PRINT AT 9,0
110 PRINT INK 1; "The area is "
120 PRINT TAB 3;INK 3;x*y
```

```
130 PRINT AT 13,5
140 PRINT INK 2;"What's the length of the shorter sides?"
150 INPUT answer1
160 PRINT AT 13,5
170 PRINT INK 2;"What's the length of the longer sides? "
180 INPUT answer2
190 IF answer1=x AND answer2=y THEN GO TO 500
200 PRINT AT 16,10
210 PRINT INK 3;TAB 4;FLASH 1;" Sorry – you're wrong "
220 PRINT AT 17,0
230 PRINT INK 3;TAB 4;FLASH1;"The CORRECT answers are "
240 PRINT INK 2;TAB 12;x;' & ';y
250 PAUSE 300
260 GO TO 20
500 PRINT AT 15,10
510 PRINT
520 PRINT TAB 10;INK 1;FLASH 1;" Well done! "
530 FOR n=1 TO 30
540 BORDER INT (RND*8)
550 BEEP .01,(INT (RND*80))−40
560 NEXT n
570 BORDER 7
580 GO TO 20
```

13. SOLUTIONS

OLD MASTERS

1. 40 talents.

2. The donkey had five and the mule seven sacks.

3. 28 scholars.

4. The minimum number of apples per basket is 4, but any multiple of 4 provides any equally valid solution.

5. 60 years old.

6. The 'obvious' solution, 3 piastres and 5 piastres, is wrong. The 8 piastres was in payment for 2⅔ loaves. Therefore one loaf is worth 3 piastres. Since each ate 2⅔ loaves, the first shepherd gave ⅓ of a loaf to the hunter, and the other shepherd gave 2⅓. Therefore 1 piastre should go to the first shepherd, and 7 piastres to the second shepherd.

7. 27.

8. 19.2 yards.

9. 54 ducats.

10. 92 ducats.

11. 29 ducats.

12. The value of a barrel is 110 francs, and the duty payable is 10 francs.

13.
In Shylock's bargain for the flesh was found
No mention of the blood that flowed around:
So when the stick was sawed in pieces eight,
The sawdust lost diminished from the weight.

14. One. In this genealogy, which demonstrates the relationships, males are denoted by capitals, and females by small letters. The governor is E and his guest is C

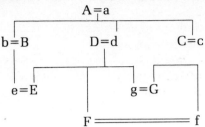

15.
24 miles; half past six.

A level mile takes quarter of an hour, up hill one third, down hill one sixth. Hence to go and return over the same mile, whether on the level or on the hill-side, takes half an hour. Hence in six hours they went 12 miles out and 12 back. If the 12 miles out had been nearly all level, they would have taken a little over 3 hours; if nearly all up hill, a little under 4. Hence 3½ hours must be within half an hour of the time taken in reaching the peak; thus, as they started at 3, they got there with half an hour of half past six.

16. (a) 19 (b) The easterly traveller met 12, the other 8.

17.
5½, 6½, 7, 4½, 3½.

The sum of all the weighings, 61 lbs, includes sack 3 thrice and each of the others twice. Deducting twice the sum of the first and fourth weighings, i.e. 21 lbs for thrice 3 — i.e. 7 lbs for sack 3. The rest follows.

18. The order is M, L, Z.

19. 60 yards by 60½ yards.

20. 10 per cent.

21. 15 and 18.

22. As the monkey climbs, the weight will rise by the same amount.

23.
(a) The weight is sent down; the empty basket comes up.
(b) The son goes down; the weight comes up.
(c) The weight is taken out; the daughter goes down; the son up.

(d) The son gets out; the weight goes down; the empty basket up.
(e) The queen goes down; daughter and weight come up; daughter gets out.
(f) The weight goes down; empty basket up.
(g) Son goes down; weight comes up.
(h) Daughter removes weight, and goes down; son comes up.
(i) Son sends down weight; empty basket comes up.
(j) The son goes down; weight comes up.
(k) Son gets out; the weight falls to the ground.

24.

In the puzzle of the young stenographer's salary, she gains $12.50 the first year, but after that loses steadily. Some puzzlists fall into the error of adding the whole of each raise in a lump sum at the end of every six months, whereas the salary was raised each time to a yearly basis of $25 better, which is only an improvement of $12.50 every six months. Of course a raise of $100 per year would give the stenographer in five years, $600 plus $700 plus $800 plus $900 plus $1,000, equalling $4,000. Instead of which the stenographer loses $437.50 by her own plan, as follows:

		Yearly basis
First six months	$300.00	$600
Second six months	312.50	625
Third six months	325.00	650
Fourth six months	337.50	675
Fifth six months	350.00	700
Sixth six months	362.50	725
Seventh six months	375.00	750
Eighth six months	387.50	775
Ninth six months	400.00	800
Tenth six months	412.50	825

25.

Out of the 216 equally probable ways the dice may be thrown, you will win on only 91 of them, lose on 125. So your chance of winning at least as much as you bet is 91/216, your chance of losing 125/216.

If the dice always showed different numbers, the game would be a fair one. Suppose each square is covered with a dollar. The operator would, on each roll that showed three different numbers, take in three dollers and pay out three. But on doubles he makes a dollar and on triples he makes two dollars. In the long run, for every dollar wagered by a player, regardless of how he places the money and in what amounts, he can expect to lose about 7.8 cents. This gives the operator a profit of 7.8 per cent on each dollar bet.

26.
Hank had 11 animals, Jim 7, and Duke 21, making 39 animals altogether.

27.
From the facts given we can conclude that Jack eats lean pork at the rate of 1 barrel in 10 weeks, therefore he would finish the half-barrel of lean in 5 weeks. During this same period, his wife (who eats fat at a rate of 1 barrel in 12 weeks) would consume 5/12 of a barrel of fat. This would leave 1/12 of a barrel of fat for both of them to eat at a rate of 1 barrel in 60 days. They would finish the fat in 5 days, so the total amount of time would be 35 days plus 5 days, or 40 days altogether.

28.
The ball would travel a distance of 218.7777.... feet, or 218 feet, 9⅓ inches.

29.
Susie paid five cents for silk, four cents for worsted.

30.
The number of children on the carousel, including Sammy himself, was thirteen.

31.
Last year Mrs Wiggs raised 11,025 cabbages on a square with 105 patches on the side. This year she will raise 11,236 cabbages on a square with 106 patches on the side.

32.
In that interesting problem of the reapers who cut a swath around a rectangular field until half the crop was gathered, I find that they had a simple rule. They said: 'One-quarter the difference between a short cut cross lots, and round by the road.' Mathematicians will understand it better if we say: from the sum of the two sides subtract the diagonal of the field and divide the remainder by four.

The field was 2,000 yards long by 1,000 yards wide. Using a tape line, those honest farmers found that the diagonal from one corner to the opposite one was a little over 2,236 yards. To go 'round by the road', of course, was 3,000 yards, so the difference was a little less than 764 yards. One-quarter of this is just a bit shy of 191 yards (190.983), which is the width the border strip should be.

33. The land was divided into 18 lots.

34. Sam Loyd's Boxes

1. Sam Loyd writes: 'The original problem is impossible to solve except by such skullduggery as turning the 6 and 9 blocks upside down. One of the puzzle's peculiarities is that any such interchange involving two blocks immediately converts the puzzle to a solvable one. In fact, any odd number of interchanges has the same effect, whereas an even number leaves the puzzle unsolvable as before.'

2. 44 moves are required to get the vacant square in the top left-hand corner: 14, 11, 12, 8, 7, 6, 10, 12, 8, 7, 4, 3, 6, 4, 7, 14, 11, 15, 13, 9, 12, 8, 4, 10, 8, 4, 14, 11, 15, 13, 9, 12, 4, 8, 5, 4, 8, 9, 13, 14, 10, 6, 2, 1.

3. 39 moves are required to solve the third problem: 14, 15, 10, 6, 7, 11, 15, 10, 13, 9, 5, 1, 2, 3, 4, 8, 12, 15, 10, 13, 9, 5, 1, 2, 3, 4, 8, 12, 15, 14, 13, 9, 5, 1, 2, 3, 4, 8, 12.

4. The magic square can be produced in fifty moves: 12, 8, 4, 3, 2, 6, 10, 9, 13, 15, 14, 12, 8, 4, 7, 10, 9, 14, 12, 8, 4, 7, 10, 9, 6, 2, 3, 10, 9, 6, 5, 1, 2, 3, 6, 5, 3, 2, 1, 13, 14, 3, 2, 1, 13, 14, 3, 12, 15, 3.

5. This puzzle can be solved in 23 moves – the fewest possible. Move the blocks in the following order: A, B, F, E, C, A, B, F, E, C, A, B, D, H, G, A, B, D, H, G, D, E, F.

35. The time must have been 5⁵⁄₁₁ minutes past two o'clock.

36.
The correct and only answer is that 11,616 ladies made proposals of marriage. Here are all the details, which the reader can check for himself with the original statements. Of 10,164 spinsters, 8,085 married bachelors, 627 married widowers, 1,221 were declined by bachelors, and 231 declined by widowers. Of the 1,452 widows, 1,155 married bachelors, and 297 married widowers. No widows were declined. The problem is not difficult, by algebra, when once we have succeeded in correctly stating it.

37.
The nine men, A, B, C, D, E, F, G, H, J, all go 40 miles together on the one gallon in their engine tanks, when A transfers 1 gallon to each of the other eight and has 1 gallon left to return home. The eight go another 40 miles, when B transfers 1 gallon to each of the other seven and has 2 gallons to take him home. The seven go another 40 miles, when C transfers 1 gallon to each of the six others and returns home on the remaining 3 gallons. The six go another 40 miles, when D gives each of five 1 gallon and returns home. The five go 40 miles, when E gives each of four 1 gallon and returns home. The four go another 40 miles, when F gives each of three 1 gallon and returns home. The three go 40 miles, when G gives each of two 1 gallon and returns home. The two go 40

miles, when H gives 1 gallon to J and returns home. Finally, the last man, J, goes another 40 miles and then has 9 gallons to take him home. Thus J has gone 360 miles out and home, the greatest distance in a straight line that could be reached under the conditions.

38.
The man said, 'I am going twice as deep' not 'as deep again'. That is to say, he was still going twice as deep as he had gone already, so that when he had finished, the hole would be three times its present depth. Then the answer is that at present the hole is 3 ft 6 ins deep and the man 2 ft 4 ins above ground. When completed the hole will be 10 ft 6 ins deep, and therefore the man will be 4 ft 8 ins below the surface, or twice the distance that he is now above ground.

39.
The candles must have burnt for 3¾ hours. One candle had one-sixteenth of its total length left and the other four-sixteenths.

40. The time must have been 43⁷⁄₁₁ past two o'clock.

41.
The ordinary schoolboy would correctly treat this as a quadratic equation. Here is the actual arithmetic. Double the product of the two distances from the walls. This gives us 144, which is the square of 12. The sum of the two distances is 17. If we add these two numbers, 12 and 17, together, and also subtract one from the other, we get the two answers that 29 or 5 was the radius. Consequently the diameter was 58 inches or 10 inches. But a table of the latter dimensions would be absurd. Therefore the table must have been 58 inches in diameter.

42.
The number must be the least common multiple of 1, 2, 3, etc., up to 15, that, when divided by 7, leaves the remainder 1, by 9 leaves 3, by 11 leaves 10, by 13 leaves 3, and by 14 leaves 8. Such a number is 120. The next number is 360,480, but as we have no record of a tree – especially a very young one – bearing anything like such a large number of apples, we may take 120 to be the only answer that is acceptable.

CHILD'S PLAY

43. 27 lbs.

44. JUST ONE WORD.

45. I have built my house at the North Pole.

46. Smith, where Jones had had 'had', had had 'had had'. 'Had had' had had the examiners' approval.

47. The speaker was looking at a portrait of his son.

48. Sunday.

49.
Too wise you are,
Too wise you be;
I see you are
Too wise for me.

50. Eighteen days (on the eighteenth day he would reach the top and not slip back).

51. You can't dig half a hole!

52. UNDERGROUND.

53. E (the letters in the series are the initial letters of: one, two, three, four . . . and so on).

54.

6	7	2
1	5	9
8	3	4

55.

16	2	3	13
5	11	10	8
9	7	6	12
4	14	15	1

56. Four years ago.

57. 17 dogs and 26 chickens.

58. 15.

59. 3 animals.

60. The word TOBACCO.

61. It will take 7 days – each day the squirrel carries out one ear of corn and the two ears on his head.

62. 80 years.

63. 3 minutes.

64. N and T, these being the next letters of the alphabet composed solely of straight lines.

65. Water, the chemical formula being H_2O (H to O).

66. None – the longest river is the Nile.

67. 3.

68. Once – after that you'll be subtracting from 23, then from 21, and so on.

69. Father.

70. 300 miles.

71. East.

72. The nursery rhyme has been rewritten so that it does not contain a single occurrence of the letter E – usually the commonest letter in the English language.

73. 15 miles.

74. The Ten of Diamonds, the King of Hearts and the Eight of Spades.

75. One.

76. Eight – he makes seven cigarettes, smokes them, and makes another cigarette from those ends.

77. A missionary and a cannibal cross. The missionary returns. Two cannibals cross. One cannibal returns. Two missionaries cross. One missionary and one cannibal return. Two missionaries cross. One cannibal returns. The remaining two cannibals cross.

78. Bill.

79. 3.

80. 16.

81. CAR.

82. Mary (or Myra), Kate, Amy (or May), Enid, Lisa, Ruth, Cathy, Delia, Marian (or Marina).

73. Eric, Lee, Stan, Neil, Silas, Steven, Cyril, Daniel, Andrew.

84. Polo, Pool, Onion, Oboe, Ukelele, Cello, Canoe, Ease.

NUMBER PUZZLES

85. The father distributed £39. The first child received £15, the second £8, the third £10, and the fourth £6.

86. First boat – 15 minutes 45 seconds; second boat – 16 minutes.

87. 23 and 24.

88. 76, 24.

89. 10, 22, 26.

90. $55^2 = 3025$. $99^2 = 9801$.

91. Man 69 years 12 weeks; Woman 30 years 40 weeks.

92. Jim 18 hours; Bill 22½ hours.

93. The contents of the ten bags should be $1, $2, $4, $8, $16, $32, $64, $128, $256 and $489.

94. 30 (16, 8, 4, 2).

95. Potato 11 ounces, orange 7 ounces, apple 5 ounces, tomato 3 ounces, banana 2 ounces.

96. A 3240. B 2916. C 1944. D 2052. E 1728. Electors 6480.

97. 324.

98. 9 feet 2 inches.

99.
The third and fourth powers must contain 10 digits between them, so the number sought can only be 18, 19, 20 or 21. Of these, 20 and 21 are bound to duplicate zeros and ones, respectively. Testing 18 and 19 reveals that 18 is the answer. The third and fourth powers of 18 are 5832 and 104,976.

100. 1, 4, 16, 64.

101. £24, £20, £8, £28.

102. 18.

103. Abe $65, Bert $35, Cal $20.

104.
If I walk 26 steps, I need 30 seconds; and if I walk 34 steps, I need only 18 seconds. Multiply 30 by 34 and 26 by 18, and we get 1020 and 468. Divide the difference (552) by the difference between 30 seconds and 18 seconds (12 seconds). The answer is 46, the number of steps in the stairway, which descends at the rate of 1 step in 1½ seconds. The speed at which I walk on the stairs does not affect the question, as the step from which I alight will reach the bottom at a given moment, whatever I do in the meantime.

105.
The smallest such number is 35,641,667,749. Other numbers with the same properties may be found by adding multiples of 46,895,573,610 to the aforementioned number.

106.
The car, when Alex met it, would have reached the station in another six minutes. So Alex had been walking for 30 minutes. Hence, had his wife met Alex at the station, he would have arrived 24 minutes earlier at the point where he actually met the car. So he would have arrived home at 5.36.

107.
The camel lives 75 years, the carp 150, the cat 15, the dog 17, the elephant 300, the chicken 18, the horse 30, the ox 21, the guinea pig 15, the stork 100, the whale 400 years.

108. David 13 times, Jonathan 8 times.

109.
Multiply 273863 by 365 and the product is 99959995.

Working the problem backwards, any number whatever that consists of eight digits with the first four repeated is divisible by 73 (and by 137), because 73 times 137 is 10001. If it ends with 5 or 0, it is divisible by 365 (5 times 73). Taking all this into account, the highest possible product can be written down at once.

110. 40 coaches.

111. 3½ minutes.

112. Eight marks are required – at the 1, 3, 6, 13, 20, 27, 31 and 35 inch positions.

113. The second way is really the same as the first in reverse – either way it takes 40 minutes (⅔ of an hour) to burn the candle out.

114. The river is 1760 yards wide. The time that the boats stayed at their slips is of no relevance.

115. 3 and 2.

116. 20 gallons.

117.
$13 \times 62 = 26 \times 31$
$13 \times 93 = 39 \times 31$
$14 \times 82 = 28 \times 41$
$23 \times 64 = 46 \times 32$
$34 \times 86 = 68 \times 43$
$36 \times 84 = 48 \times 63$

118.
Call the children A, B, C, D and E in order of their weights, A being the lightest and E the heaviest. A and B together weigh 114 pounds, D and E together weigh 129 pounds. These four together weigh 243. The total

weight of all five is 303 pounds (add all the pairs together and divide by 4, since each child was weighed four times). Hence, C weighs 60 pounds. The lightest and next lightest but one weighed 115 pounds – hence A must be 55 pounds. The rest is straightforward. The individual weights are 55, 59, 60, 63 and 66 pounds.

119. $123 - 45 - 67 + 89 = 100$ (using three signs).

120. $98 - 76 + 54 + 3 + 21 = 100$ (using four signs).

121. The father and mother were both 36. The three children – triplets – were all 6 years old.

122. Joe's share was 264, Jack's 198, and Jim's 308. Their ages are 6, 4½ and 7 years, respectively.

123. $32,547,891 \times 6 = 195,287,346$.

124.
1,680   (1681 is the square of 41, 841 is the square of 29).
57,120   (57,121 is the square of 239, 28,461 is the square of 169).
1,940,448   (1,940,449 is the square of 1,393, 970,225 is the square of 985).

125.
If a square number ends in identical digits, those digits must be 4. But it is not possible for there to be more than three identical digits, so the solution is 1444 (the square of 38).

126.
There are many possible solutions for each fraction. Here are some representative solutions:

(a)	$\dfrac{5832}{17496}$	(b)	$\dfrac{3942}{15768}$	(c)	$\dfrac{2769}{13845}$	(d)	$\dfrac{2943}{17658}$
(e)	$\dfrac{2394}{16758}$	(f)	$\dfrac{3187}{25496}$	(g)	$\dfrac{6381}{57429}$		

127.
Since each letter is a final digit, they must be 1, 3, 7 and 9. A and C must be 1 or 7, otherwise the numbers ADDD and AACA would be divisible by 3. Thus B and D must be 3 or 9.

BCDB, thus, may be 3193, 3793, 9139 or 9739. But 3193 is divisible by 31 and 9139 is divisible by 13. So BCDB may be 3793 or 9739 – in both cases, C = 7 and hence A = 1.

BDAC must be 9317 or 3917, but 9317 is divisible by 7, so BDAC = 3917. Therefore A = 1, B = 3, C = 7, D = 9.

128. The four primes are 1483, 4813, 4831 and 8431.

129.

$$
\begin{array}{r}
9567 \\
1085 \\
\hline
10652 \\
\end{array}
$$

130.

$$
\begin{array}{r}
850 \\
850 \\
29786 \\
\hline
31486 \\
\end{array}
$$

131.

$$
\begin{array}{r}
7088062 \\
17531908 \\
\hline
24619970 \\
\end{array}
$$

132.
$$\frac{219}{3} = 73 \qquad \frac{438}{6} = 73 \qquad \frac{657}{9} = 73$$

133.

$$
\begin{array}{r}
570140 \\
6 \\
\hline
3420840 \\
\end{array}
$$

134.

$$
\begin{array}{r}
97809 \\
124 \overline{\smash{\big)}\ 12128316} \\
1116 \\
\hline
968 \\
868 \\
\hline
1003 \\
992 \\
\hline
1116 \\
1116 \\
\hline
\end{array}
$$

CIRCLES, SQUARES AND ANGLES

135.

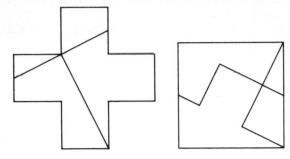

136.

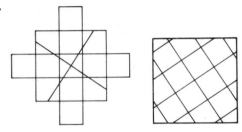

137. As shown in the diagram, eleven non-overlapping triangles can be produced by seven lines.

138.
Fold the square in half and make the crease FE. Fold the side AB so that the point B lies on FE, and you will get the points G and H, from which you can fold HGJ. While B is on G, fold AB back on AH, and you will have the line AK. You can now fold the triangle AJK, which is the largest equilateral triangle obtainable.

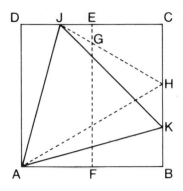

139.

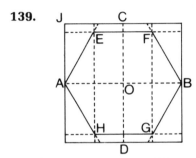

Folding the paper in half horizontally and vertically we obtain the lines AOB and COD. We then get EH and FG by folding the edges over to the centre line COD, thus bisecting AO and OB.

We fold over AJ so that J lies on the line EH – at the point E. We do the same at the other three corners to obtain the points F, G and H.

Then it is a simple matter to fold AE, EF, FB, BG, GH and HA to give the hexagon AEFBGH.

140. 8.

141. 157¹⁄₇ square miles approximately.

142.
Referring to the original diagram, let AC be x, let CD be x−9, and let EC be x−5. Then x−5 is a mean proportional between x−9 and x, from which we find that x=25. Therefore the diameters are 50 ins. and 41 ins. respectively.

143. 2513.28 square yards, approximately.

144.
The area of the path is exactly 66⅔ square yards, which is clearly seen if you imagine a little triangular piece cut off at the bottom and removed to

the top right corner. Here is the proof. The area of the garden is
55 × 40 = 2,200. And (55⅓ × 40) + 66⅔ also equals 2,200. Finally the
sum of the squares of 53⅓ and 40 must equal the square of 66⅔, as it
does.

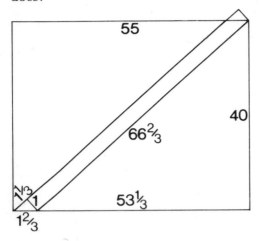

145. The triangle has integral sides of 47, 1104 and 1105 inches.

146.
The distance from the top of the ladder to the ground was ⁴⁄₅ of the
length of the ladder. Multiply the distance from the wall – 4 yards – by
the denominator of this fraction – 5 – and you get 20. Now deduct the
square of the numerator from the square of the denominator of ⁴⁄₅, and
you have 9, which is the square of 3. Finally, divide 20 by 3, and there is
the answer: 6⅔ yards.

147. The bell rope must have been 32 feet 1½ inches in length from
ceiling to floor.

148.

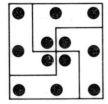

149.
Divide the diameter of the circle into four equal parts. Then describe
semicircles on each side of the diameter as shown.

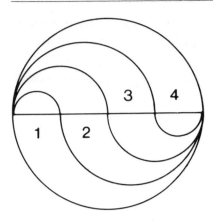

150.
As many as 22 pieces may be obtained by the 6 cuts. The illustration shows a pretty symmetrical solution.

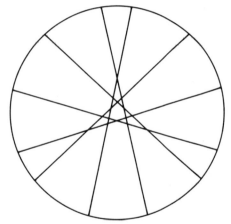

The rule in such cases is that every cut shall intersect every other cut and no two intersections coincide; that is to say, every line passes through every other line, but more than two lines do not cross at the same point anywhere. There are other ways of making the cuts, but this rule must always be observed if we are to get the full number of pieces.

151.

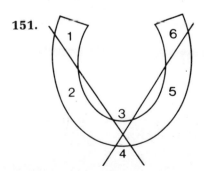

152.

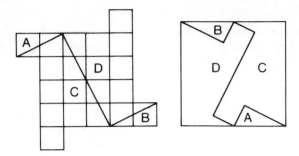

153.

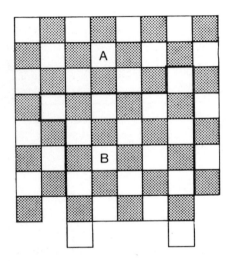

154.

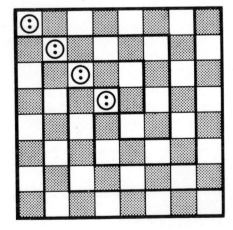

155. The diagram shows how it is done.

156.
We place 20 cigarettes in the bottom layer. In the second layer, instead of having 20, we place 19, arrange as shown in the diagram. Then we continue with alternate layers of 20 and 19.

Original method   New method

Let us suppose the diameter of a cigarette is 2 units. The second and subsequent layers, using our new method, will add only 1.732 units to the height. The depth of the box is 16 units, since it originally contained eight layers. With our new method we shall get nine layers – 2 plus 8 × 1.732 is equal to 15.856. So with five layers of 20 and four layers of 19 we shall get 176 cigarettes into the box.

THREE-DIMENSIONAL PUZZLES

157.
Move coin 1 to below the bottom row, between coins 8 and 9. Then move coins 7 and 10 to the left of coin 2 and to the right of coin 3.

158.
Move coins 6 and 7 to the left of coin 1. Move coins 3 and 4 to the right of coin 5. Move coins 7 and 1 to the right of coin 2. Move coins 4 and 8 to the right of coin 6.

159.
Each time, after turning over a coin, start again from the coin that is three further on from the coin that you have just turned over.

160.

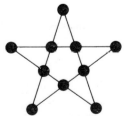

161.

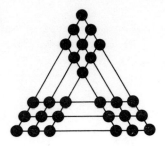

162.

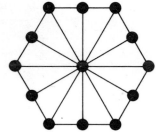

163.

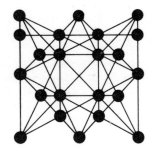

164. (1) Move from 1 to 5.
(2) Move from 3 to 7 to 1.
(3) Move from 8 to 4 to 3 to 7.
(4) Move from 6 to 2 to 8 to 4 to 3.
(5) Move from 5 to 6 to 2 to 8.
(6) Move from 1 to 5 to 6.
(7) Move from 7 to 1.

165.

166. (a)

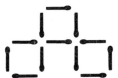

(b)

(c)

(d)

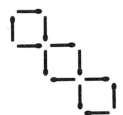

(e)

(f)

167.

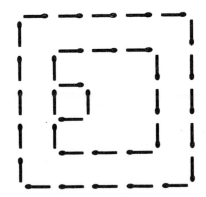

168.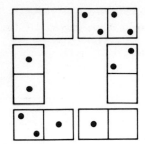

169.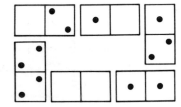

170.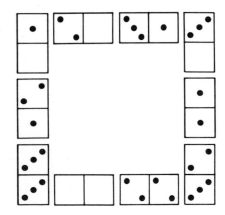

171.

172.   0/0 − 0/4 − 4/4
            0/1 − 1/4 − 4/2
            1/1 − 1/3 − 3/3
            1/2 − 2/2 − 2/3
            2/0 − 0/3 − 3/4

173.
There are several solutions for each rectangle. Here are some typical solutions.

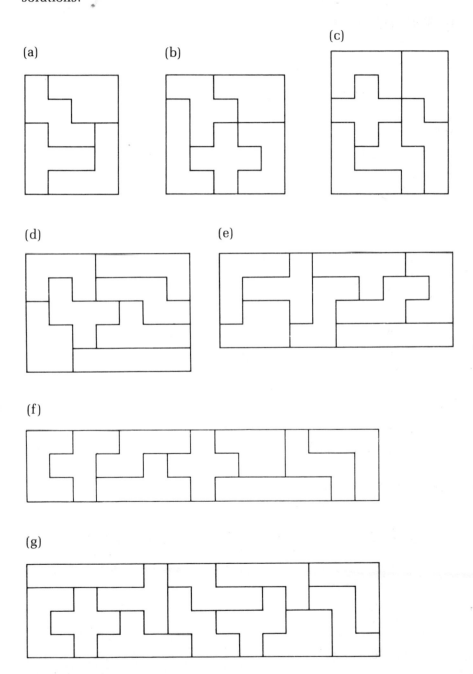

(a)

(b)

(c)

(d)

(e)

(f)

(g)

174. Here is one possible solution:

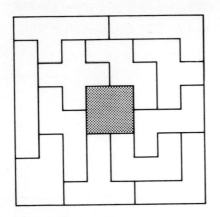

175. Here is a solution for the 'cross' pentomino.

176.
(a) 1 Q–KB1 B–N7 or Rp moves 2 Q–QN1 and 3 QxRP (or Q–R7). If 1 ... B–B6 or B–Q5 2 Q–Q3. If 1 ... B–K4 or B–B3 2 Q–KB5. If 1 ... P–N6 2 N–N6 ch PxN 3 Q–R3 mate.

(b)

	1 P–QB4	P–QB4	1 P–Q4	P–Q4
	2 Q–R4	Q–R4	2 Q–Q3	Q–Q3
	3 Q–B6	Q–B6	3 Q–KR3	Q–KR3
	4 QxB	mate	4 QxB	mate

(c) 1 P–R8=B. If 1 ... K–B1 2 P–N8=Q ch. If 1 ... K–K1 2 K–K6. If 1 ... K–N1 2 K–N6.

(d) 1 B–B5 NxB 2 Q–QR7 any 3 Q–N1 mate. If 1 . . . any other move 2 Q–Q7 and 3 Q–Q1 mate.

(e) (i) Black's KR8 (ii) Black's K6 (iii) Black's QR1 (iv) Black's KN2.

177.   43 – 23
             45 – 43
             53 – 33
             23 – 43
             42 – 44

178.   45 – 47
             43 – 45
             64 – 44 – 46
             24 – 44
             47 – 45 – 43
             42 – 44

179.   54 – 74
             43 – 63
             44 – 46
             34 – 36 – 56 – 54
             15 – 35
             75 – 73 – 53 – 55
             65 – 45 – 25 – 23 – 43
             42 – 44

180.   42 – 44   45 – 25
             23 – 43   65 – 45
             31 – 33   57 – 55
             34 – 32   45 – 65
             51 – 31 – 33   47 – 45
             43 – 23   13 – 33
             45 – 43   14 – 34
             64 – 44   15 – 35
             52 – 54   73 – 53
             44 – 64   74 – 54
             25 – 45   75 – 55
             37 – 35

LOGIC PUZZLES

181.
Either man should be asked the following question: 'If I were to ask you if this is the way I should go, would you say yes?' While asking the question, the hiker should be pointing at either of the directions going from the fork.

182.
The clerk gave back 5 dollars and kept 25 dollars. The boy gave each man 1 dollar and kept 2 dollars. Each man paid 9 dollars which, less the 2 dollars kept by the boy, makes the 25 dollars given to the clerk.

183.
On the second evening King Arthur arranged the knights and himself in the following order round the table: A, F, B, D, G, E, C. On the third evening they sat thus: A, E, B, G, C, F, D.

He thus had B next but one to him (the nearest possible) on both occasions, and G was the third from him (the furthest possible) on both occasions. No other way of seating the knights would have been so satisfactory.

184.
The age of Mary to that of Ann must be in the ratio of 5 to 3. As the sum of their ages was 44, Mary was 27½ and Ann 16½.

185.
The locomotive pushes truck 1 up to the points, then returns to the opposite siding and pushes truck 2 up to truck 1 at the points. The two trucks are then pulled by the locomotive down the siding and pushed on to the main line to a position between the two sidings. Truck 1 is then uncoupled and left standing while the locomotive pulls truck 2 along the main line in order to push it up to the points where it is left. The locomotive returns to truck 1, pulls it along the main line and then pushes it up the siding to its required final position. The locomotive then proceeds up the other siding to the points to pull truck 2 to its required position, then uncouples and returns to the main line.

186.
The engine that has had its fire drawn and therefore cannot move is No. 5. Move the other engines in the following order: 7, 6, 3, 7, 6, 1, 2, 4, 1, 3, 8, 1, 3, 2, 4, 3, 2 – seventeen moves in all, leaving the engines in the required order.

187.
Jennifer, the blonde hairdresser, is the oldest; Jane, the brunette receptionist, comes next; and Judy, the red-headed typist, is the youngest.

188.
(c) Viktor can outlift Boris by more than he can outlift Tam.

189.
The musician is Bertram Fuller.

Here is an outline of the solution, giving only the successive conclusions: Dwight is Mr Hooper, Clint is the accountant, Bertram is the musician, Ambrose is the priest, Dwight Hooper is the doctor, Ambrose is not Mr Grimm, Mr Eastwood is Ambrose, Clint is not Mr Fuller, Clint is Mr Grimm (the accountant), and Bertram Fuller is the musician.

190.
Diana lives two miles from Ann, and Cathy Black is the oldest of the four girls.

191.
(a) John is an advertising man; Paul is an actor; George is an auditor.
(b) Harry the actor is older than Dick the auditor who is older than Tom the advertising man.
(c) George the actor earns more than David the advertising man who earns more than Lloyd the auditor.
(d) Freeman the auditor is the chairman; Hardy the actor is the treasurer; Willis the advertising man is the secretary.

192.
Cetri, 1 million, English, amethysts.
Auni, 2 million, French, coffee.
Equin, 3 million, Portuguese, dates.
Dequar, 4 million, Spanish, bananas.
Bebi, 5 million, Dutch, emeralds.

193.
Carpet Fitting by Matt Coates has a yellow cover and 170 pages.
Indoor Heating by Celia Holmes has a white cover and 190 pages.
Domestic Insulation by Anita Lawn has a red cover and 220 pages.
Painting and Decorating by Bernard Cole has a green cover and 240 pages.
Improve Your Garden by Walter Wall has a blue cover and 300 pages.

194.
1. No acrobatic feat which involves turning a quadruple somersault is ever attempted in a circus.
2. No bird in this aviary lives on mince-pies.
3. All your poems are uninteresting.
4. Rainy days are always cloudy.
5. No badger can guess a conundrum.
6. I always avoid a kangaroo.

VISUAL PUZZLES

195. The distance from A to B is the same as the distance from B to C.

196. They are all equal.

197.
(a) It is impossible to say whether the cube is viewed from above or below – it could be either.
(b) The line is perfectly straight.

198. AC and BD are the same length.

199. All three are the same length.

200. All five are equal in area.

201. The two circles are the same size.

202. Despite the evidence of your eyes, both horizontal lines are the same length.

203.

204. There is only one route to the centre.

205.

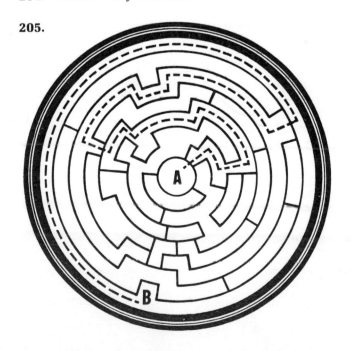

206. There are 640 routes to the centre.

207.

208. (a)

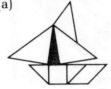

(b)

(c)

(d)

(e)

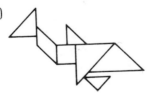

(f)

(h)

(g)

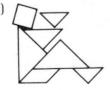

(i)      (j)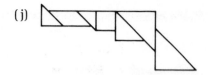

209.

210.

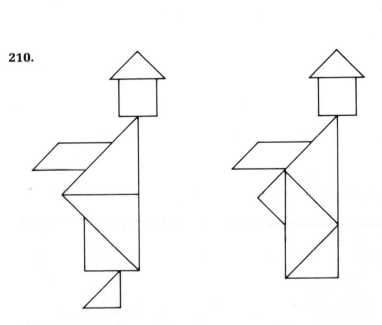

WORDPLAY

211. 1. SMART   2. CROP   3. BRACE   4. CONVERSE   5. OBJECTIVE
6. UTTER

212. 1. GAG 2. DEED 3. NOON 4. SHAHS 5. DEIFIED 6. TENET

213.
1. SOAK & WET 2. TIE & BIND 3. FLOG & BEAT 4. RAGE & ANGER
5. SEAR & CHAR 6. ACID & SOUR 7. AVER & ASSERT 8. LEAVE &
QUIT 9. SPIN & GYRATE 10. FLIRT & COQUET.

214. The past tense of the eight verbs all rhyme with TAUT.

215. WITHHOLD, SKIING, BOOKKEEPER, VACUUM, NAVVY,
POWWOW.

216.
There are several 7-letter words: ACCEDED, BAGGAGE, CABBAGE,
DEFACED and EFFACED. There is also at least one 8-letter word:
CABBAGED.

217.

ZEBRA	OCTET	BLISS
ERROR	CRIME	LUNCH
BRING	TIRED	INTER
RONDO	EMEND	SCENE
ARGON	TEDDY	SHREW

218. YEA, A PIED, SUNDAE, WEIGH, QUAI, OK, SOLEIL,
DOSSIER, BEAUJOLAIS, SOBRIQUET, DAY, CHEZ.

219.

OIL,	COIL,	COLIC.	SEAR,	SCARE,	SCARCE.
HAT,	CHAT,	CATCH.	SOUR,	SCOUR,	CROCUS.
ARK,	RACK,	CRACK.	LEAN,	LANCE,	CANCEL.
IRK,	RICK,	CRICK.	HATE,	C H E A T,	CACHET.
TAPE,	EPACT,	ACCEPT.	HEAD,	ACHED,	CACHED.
OUST,	SCOUT,	STUCCO.	RILE,	RELIC,	CIRCLE.
OAST,	COAST,	ACCOST.	LOUT,	CLOUT,	OCCULT.
ROSE,	SCORE,	SOCCER.	SPITE,	SEPTIC,	SCEPTIC.
HERE,	CHEER,	CRECHE.	NOSE,	SCONE,	SCONCE.
NEAR,	CRANE,	CANCER.	NEAT,	ENACT,	ACCENT.

220. (a) DOLPHIN
(b) GRAVITY
(c) DIALECT

221. (a) LETTUCE, SPINACH
(b) BERMUDA, ICELAND

222.
(a) NEVADA (b) MAINE (c) MARYLAND (d) WASHINGTON
(e) MINNESOTA (f) RHODE ISLAND (g) INDIANA
(h) PENNSYLVANIA (i) RHODE ISLAND (j) SOUTH CAROLINA.

223.

(a)	(b)
COAST	BRING
BOAST	BRINK
BEAST	DRINK
LEAST	DRUNK
LEASE	TRUNK
LEAVE	TRUCK
HEAVE	TRICK
HEAVY	THICK

224.   (a) SANATORIUM, SANITARIUM
(b) DESCRY, DECRY
(c) MENDICITY, MENDACITY
(d) ADJURE, ABJURE
(e) ABRADE, UPBRAID
(f) DISCOMFIT, DISCOMFORT
(g) VENAL, VENIAL
(h) INDITE, INDICT
(i) COMPLACENT, COMPLAISANT
(j) BIENNIAL, BIANNUAL

225. DEFYING, FIGHTING, HIJACK, MONOPOLY,
QUERIST, UNDERSTUDY, OXYGENIZE.

226.
(a) ADDER (1 letter back) (b) CHAIN (6 letters back) (c) FILLS (6 letters back) (d) MILLS (6 letters back) (e) COBRA (3 letters back) (f) BANJO (4 letters back) (g) CHEER (7 letters back) (h) SNEER (1 letter back) (i) SHEER (1 letter back) (j) PECAN (4 letters back).

227.
There are many possible answers but here are mine: (a) 12344 – GLASS; 11232 – LLAMA; 12123 – COCOA; 12132 – MAMBA; 12133 – AMASS; 12213 – ALLAY; 12231 – SEEDS; 12233 – COOEE; 12312 – VERVE; 12313 – ENDED; 12323 – CEDED; 12331 – TWEET; 12332 – MANNA; 11231 – EERIE; 12113 – LULLS; 12131 – RARER; 12311 – FLUFF; 12232 – ERROR; 12322 – LEVEE; 12112 – MAMMA.

(b) 123232 – BANANA; 123321 – REDDER; 122132 – TEETHE; 122323 – NEEDED; 122131 – EFFETE; 121223 – COCOON; 121133 – TATTOO; 122321 – DEEMED; 123443 – GROTTO; 123123 – MURMUR; 123212 – REVERE; 123344 – TOFFEE.

228.
(a) 4-letter examples: RASH, RISK.
     5-letter examples: TOPAZ, WEEPS.
     7-letter example: WETTISH.
(b) TYPEWRITER is usually considered to be the longest word using the letters on the top row. There are several other 10-letter words though – REPERTOIRE, PROPRIETOR and PERPETUITY – and there are also a couple of 11-letter words – PROPRIETORY and RUPTUREWORT.
(c) The longest common word is FLASKS. Longer, though less common, words are HALAKAH, FLAGFALL and HAGGADAH.

229. (a) ABSTEMIOUS
       (b) There are other possible solutions, but these are probably the most common words:

AIEOU – Ambidextrous	EUOIA – Pneumonia
OEAUI – Overhauling	EUAIO – Reputation
AUIOE – Cautioned	OAUIE – Consanguine
AIOUE – Anxiousness	OUEAI – Housemaid
EOUAI – Encouraging	UAIOE – Ultraviolet
IOUAE – Discourage	UOIAE – Unsociable

230.
1. J-AIL 2. A-GREED 3. N-EARLY 4. E-MOTION 5. A-STERN 6. U-SURER 7. S-IMPLY 8. T-ROUBLES 9. E-STRANGE 10. N-EAT. (JANE AUSTEN)

231.
(a) SENATOR (b) BIOGENY (c) SYBARITE (d) GAINSAYS
(e) CALUMNIES (f) INDICATORY (g) GABARDINE (h) SCHEMATIC
(i) ENIGMATIST (j) DESECRATION (k) INTOXICATE (l) ALLEGORIST
(m) INTERLACES (n) CONTAINERISED (o) PETROCHEMICAL
(p) PREDICTIVENESS.

232. CRESCENT (CRESS, SCENT).

233. BUTTERFLY (BUTT, TURF, FLY).

234. CARES, CARESS.

235.
1. NAPLES 2. ELBE 3. WASHINGTON 4. CINCINNATI 5. AMSTER-
DAM 6. STAMBOUL 7. TORNEA 8. LEPANTO 9. ECLIPTIC.
This gives NEWCASTLE and COALMINES.

236.
(a)	WET, bet, bey, dey, DRY.
(b)	EYE, dye, die, did, LID.
(c)	EEL, e'en, pen, pin, PIE.
(d)	RAVEN, riven, risen, riser, MISER.
(e)	OAT, rat, rot, roe, RYE.
(f)	TEA, sea, set, sot, HOT.
(g)	PIG, wig, wag, way, say, STY.
(h)	FISH, fist, gist, girt, gird, BIRD.
(i)	REST, lest, lost, loft, soft, SOFA.
(j)	PEN, e'en, eel, ell, ill, ilk, INK.
(k)	NOSE, note, cote, core, corn, coin, CHIN.
(l)	TEARS, sears, stars, stare, stale, stile, SMILE.
(m)	PITCH, pinch, winch, wench, tench, tenth, TENTS.
(n)	POOR, boor, book, rook, rock, rick, RICH.
(o)	APE, are, ere, err, ear, mar, MAN.
(p)	FLOUR, floor, flood, blood, brood, broad, BREAD.
(q)	MINE, mint, mist, most, moat, coat, COAL.
(r)	FURIES, buries, buried, burked, barked, barred, BARREL.
(s)	WHEAT, cheat, cheap, cheep, creep, creed, breed, BREAD.
(t)	FOUR, foul, fool, foot, fort, fore, fire, FIVE.
(u)	HARE, hark, hack, sack, sock, soak, soap, SOUP.
(v)	PITY, pits, pins, fins, find, fond, food, GOOD.
(w)	BLACK, blank, blink, clink, chink, chine, whine, WHITE.
(x)	COMB, come, home, hole, hale, hall, hail, HAIR.
(y)	WHIP, whit, wait, want, cant, cast, last, LASH.
(z)	SHOES, shops, chops, crops, cross, cress, crest, CRUST.
(aa)	BREAD, break, bleak, bleat, blest, blast, boast, TOAST.
(bb)	STEAL, steel, steer, sheer, shier, shies, shins, chins, COINS.
(cc)	TREE, free, flee, fled, feed, weed, weld, wold, WOOD.
(dd)	GRASS, crass, cress, tress, trees, frees, freed, greed, GREEN.
(ee)	ELM, ell, all, ail, air, fir, far, oar, OAK.
(ff)	ARMY, arms, aims, dims, dams, dame, name, nave, NAVY.
(gg)	BEANS, beams, seams, shams, shame, shale, shall, shell, SHELF.
(hh)	BUY, bud, bid, aid, aim, arm, ark, ask, ASS.
(ii)	ONE, owe, ewe, eye, dye, doe, toe, too, TWO.

(jj) CAIN, chin, shin, spin, spun, spud, sped, aped, abed, ABEL.

(kk) BLUE, glue, glut, gout, pout, port, part, pant, pint, PINK.

(ll) COSTS, posts, pests, tests, tents, tenth, tench, teach, peach, peace, PENCE.

(mm) LOAF, leaf, deaf, dear, deer, dyer, dyes, eyes, eves, even, OVEN.

(nn) KETTLE, settle, settee, setter, better, betted, belted, bolted, bolter, bolder, HOLDER.

(oo) ROGUE, vogue, vague, value, valve, halve, helve, heave, leave, lease, least, BEAST.

(pp) QUELL, quill, quilt, guilt, guile, guide, glide, glade, grade, grave, brave, BRAVO.

(qq) RIVER, rover, cover, coves, cores, corns, coins, chins, shins, shine, shone, SHORE.

(rr) WITCH, winch, wench, tench, tenth, tents, tints, tilts, tills, fills, falls, fails, fairs, FAIRY.

237.
1. WHIST 2. ISSUE 3. STAIN 4. CAPON 5. OUNCE 6. NAILS 7. SLIPS 8. INURE 9. NORSE.
States: WISCONSIN, TENNESSEE, LOUISIANA.

CROSSWORDS AND FRIENDS

238.

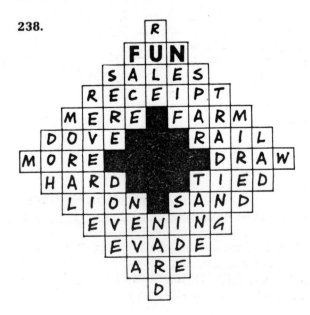

239.
Horizontal: 1. FIG 4. CANOE 6. WARFARE 8. MARMALADE 10. E.G.
11. EA 12. SOLUTION 17. SNAG 18. CAST 19. SHEET 20. SO 22. OR
23. NORFOLK 29. FIRPO 30. POE.
Vertical: 1. FARM 2. INFANT 3. GOAL 4. CAR 5. ERA 6. WAGON
7. EDENS 8. MESSES 9. EASTER 13. LAS 14. UGH 15. ICE 16. OAT
21. ON 22. O.K. 24. OF 25. RIP 26. FRO 27. OPE 28. LO.

240.

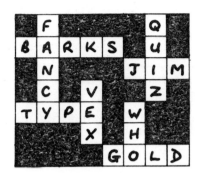

241.

Notes
Across: 15. REV. NONSENSE SONGS, PREFACE, 'HE WEARETH A
RUNCIBLE HAT'. 19. RAND 23. HAMLET I 1 166 25. LION 26. LOVE'S
LABOUR'S LOST IV 1 79. 28. PEER 44 and 48. LAY ABOUT IT. 53. THE
TWO KEANS.
Down: 7 REV. & 5. MOTE 10. LION 18. BR. ROUND LEA 21. I'M IN D.S.,
DAL SEGNO 27. FRANCIS THOMPSON, MISTRESS OF VISION, XIII
36. TUT(OR) 41. D-YES 43. ANCIENT MARINER, II 45. REV.
CHICK-PEA, PEAHEN 50 & 47. I.E. POUCHED RAT.

242.
Across: 1. NOMAD 4. PARKER 8. MALODOUR 9. OILED 11. SODIUM
12. CALENDS 13. ABSTRACT 14. TARRY 15. CHEROOTS
19. RENEGADE 22. GNOME 24. VILLAGER 27. EMBRACE 28. UNFELT
29. DIXIE 30. SECRETS 31. DANDLE 32. HERDS.
Down: 1. NABOB 2. MONITOR 3. DOGMA 4. PRACTISE 5. ROULETTE
6. KINEMA 7. RENDERED 8. MOSAIC 10. DUSTY 16. HANDMAID
17. OVERAWED 18. TRAVERSE 20. GRAFTER 21. EARTHS 22. GREED
23. MARGIN 25. LURCH 26. ELVES.

243.
Across: 1. CAULD 5. SCIRPUS 11. JARGONELLE 12. CHUPATTY
14. KIWI 15. STAMMEL 16. STALAG 18. LOBED 19. HOPLITE
24. ERRATIC 25. CHUTE 26. PARENT 28. RESPIRE 30. EDGE
31. ZEMINDAR 32. SCREENINGS 33. SPENDER 34. GOTHS.
Down: 1. COCKSHY 2. ACHITOPHEL 3. LARPILLI 4. DRAMA
6. COTTIER 7. INYALA 8. REAM 9. PLUMBITE 10. SEELD
13. WEEPING ASH 17. APLUSTRE 20. TERRENE 21. MARENGO
22. ICTERUS 23. SEIZED 25. CROSS 27. AWING 29. PEEN.

244.
Back: 1. NEEDY 2. HINDERS 3. LITERAL 4. PLAIN 6. GIVES
8. DILUTED 12. PLAYED 14. DIVIDE 15. ILLNESS 16. SWEET
17. POLAR 18. FAILURE 22. CAREFUL 25. RAPID.
Up: 5. VERSE 7. TENSE 8. DEPTH 9. ADULTS 10. DISPLAY
11. LIGHTEN 13. VILLAIN 19. LORDS 20. FALSELY 21. REPEL
22. CREDIT 23. DOUBTED 24. PRIDE 25. REFUSED.

245.
Across: 1. ETRUSCAN 5. DESERT 9. RESPECTS 10. PIERCE
11. HINDLEGS 12. ARTIST 14. UNDERSIGNS 18. PERMISSION
22. RAGGED 23. NAMELESS 24. DETOUR 25. DISPERSE 26. CANTER
27. ANGRIEST.
Down: 1. EARTHY 2. RESENT 3. STEALS 4. ANTAGONIST
6. EDITRESS 7. EARNINGS 8. TREATISE 13. DECORATION
15. SPORADIC 16. BRIGHTEN 17. SINECURE 19. DEEPER 20. DECREE
21. ASSERT.

246.
(a) **Across:** 1. CENTAUR 5. PICADOR 6. INSTEAD 7. ELAPSES
    Down: 1. CAPSIZE 2. NICOSIA 3. ADDRESS 4. REREDOS
(b) **Across:** 1. COMMONS 5. OLIVIER 6. PERSIAN 7. RETINUE
    Down: 1. CROPPER 2. MAIGRET 3. OPINION 4. STRANGE

247.

F	A	U	L	T	■	S	H	I	S	H	■	E	R	A
A	R	M	O	R	■	P	O	N	T	O	O	N	E	D
R	O	B	L	E	■	I	N	T	E	R	L	U	D	E
O	M	E	L	E	T	T	E	■	M	A	I	M	S	■
S	A	R	I	■	R	E	S	T	S	■	V	E	T	O
■	■	P	R	E	S	T	O	■	S	E	R	A	C	
S	I	M	O	O	M	■	Y	A	L	E	■	A	R	T
A	D	A	P	T	O	R	■	D	I	N	E	T	T	E
C	E	N	■	A	R	I	D	■	F	O	R	E	S	T
H	A	I	R	S	■	G	E	N	E	R	A	■		
A	L	F	A	■	C	A	P	E	R	■	S	A	G	A
■	S	O	N	A	R	■	L	A	S	T	A	G	E	S
M	O	L	E	C	U	L	A	R	■	A	B	A	S	H
U	N	D	E	R	M	I	N	E	■	E	L	I	T	E
M	S	S	■	E	B	B	E	D	■	L	E	N	E	S

248.

Q	U	A	F	F	E	D	■	S	C	A	R	E	R	
U	N	D	E	R	G	O	■	S	T	I	B	I	N	E
E	N	D	E	A	R	S	■	T	E	T	R	O	D	E
R	E	I	S	■	E	S	C	A	P	E	■	R	U	N
I	R	S	■	S	T	E	R	N	S	■	G	I	R	T
E	V	O	K	E	■	D	I	D	■	P	E	T	E	R
D	E	N	I	A	L	■	M	I	L	I	T	A	R	Y
■	T	R	I	T	E	N	E	S	S	■				
F	U	R	B	E	L	O	W	■	S	T	U	P	O	R
I	L	I	A	D	■	W	A	S	■	O	P	I	N	E
R	U	N	G	■	C	A	V	E	I	N	■	R	E	V
E	L	K	■	F	I	B	E	R	S	■	T	O	P	I
D	A	M	F	O	O	L	■	I	L	L	E	G	A	L
O	T	A	R	I	N	E	■	F	E	A	T	U	R	E
G	E	N	I	E	S	■	S	T	R	E	E	T	S	

249.
A. Value B. Intent C. Ludo D. Loaf E. Earth F. Tees G. Teddy H. Eyes
J. Cuban K. Hosts L. Anthem M. Ragtime N. Lewd P. Organ Q. Thing
R. Trust S. Etch T. Brief U. Rash V. Outset W. Nigh X. Theft Y. Ether.

Quotation: 'These struggles with the natural character, the strong native bent of the heart, may seem futile and fruitless but in the end they do good.'
Villette, Charlotte Brontë.

250.
A. Twister B. Haddock C. Entrance D. Reveals E. Asking F. Infidel
G. Nowhere H. Bursting J. Oratory K. Whippet L. Dusty M. Hamper
N. Lawful P. Absinthe Q. Wealth R. Repair S. Ewes T. Norfolk U. Coward V. Espying.
Quotation: 'In Autumn the partridges whirred up, birds in flocks blew like spray across the fallow, rooks appeared on the grey watery heavens and flew cawing into the winter.'
The Rainbow, D. H. Lawrence.

251.
1. Modest 2. Destroyer 3. Ermine 4. Neptune 5. Nevertheless 6. Essential 7. Altitude 8. Deluge 9. Geisha 10. Handicap 11. Capable
12. Leveret 13. Retriever 14. Verbatim 15. Immense 16. Semaphore
17. Oregon 18. Onerous 19. Usurper 20. Permafrost 21. Stipend
22. Endeavour 23. Urbane 24. Nectar 25. Artisan 26. Andiron
27. Onager 28. Erudite 29. Tempest 30. Stiletto 31. Toxin 32. Indigo
33. Goliath.

252.

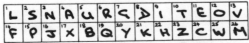

QUICK THINKING

253. -7.2.

254. 1, 2, 3.

255. Give the fifth person the basket with the apple still in it.

256. $1^3 + 12^3$. $9^3 + 10^3$.

257. Inches in a mile (63,360 to about 52,000).

258. Seconds in a week (604,800 to 528,000).

259. 1 ton.

260. 250 centimetres.

261. They are both the same.

262. (a) 666 days.
    (b) 666 inches.
    (c) 28 days.
    (d) 666 millimetres.
    (e) One-fourteenth of a week.

263. He cannot average 60 miles per hour for the two laps – unless he covers the second lap in no time at all!

264. 100. The fractions cancel out to leave one-tenth of 1000.

265. 8.

266. 8.

267. Push the cork *into* the bottle, then shake out the coin.

268.

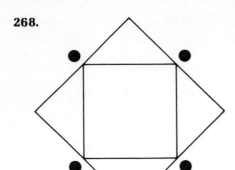

The diagram shows how it may be done.

269.

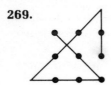

270. No. I would take your £2, say 'I lose', and give you £1. You would have won the bet but lost £1.

271. A gets to the station first. B probably misses the train.

272. Four boys and three girls.

273. Thirty-five.

274. 504.

275. 2,001,000.

276. 14.7 times. (This is found by taking the sum of 1 + 6/5 + 6/4 + 6/3 + 6/2 + 6/1).

277. He stands the signpost up so that the arm indicating the place he has come from is pointing in the correct direction. The other arms will then point correctly too.

278. 190.

279. 66 + 66 + 6 + 6.

280. (a) teepee (b) voodoo (c) assess (d) riffraff

281. (a) beekeeper (b) assessors.

MODERN MASTERS

282.
Humpty Dumpty's mark in arithmetic was 10.

There were altogether seven Good Eggs who qualified, because the number of marks necessary to qualify was $4 \times 3 \times$ the number of subjects, and at the same time twice as many as the number of Good Eggs besides Humpty Dumpty, who qualified, multiplied by the number of subjects.

There must have been at least five subjects, because the total number of marks necessary to qualify was four times the maximum obtainable in one subject and no marks were repeated in any one score.

In the case of five subjects, there are exactly seven ways to score:

$$60 = 15 + 14 + 13 + 12 + 6$$
$$60 = 15 + 14 + 13 + 11 + 7$$
$$60 = 15 + 14 + 13 + 10 + 8$$
$$60 = 15 + 14 + 12 + 11 + 8$$
$$60 = 15 + 14 + 12 + 10 + 9$$
$$60 = 15 + 13 + 12 + 11 + 9$$
$$60 = 14 + 13 + 12 + 11 + 10$$

In the case of more than five subjects, there are many more than seven ways to score.

Humpty Dumpty's mark in arithmetic, therefore, was 10.

283.
The two sides of the rectangle total 23 miles. Hence, if m miles be one side of the rectangle,

$$(m + 4)(23 - m + 5) = 2m(23 - m)$$

So m is either 14 or 8.

The Governor had had in mind a rectangle 15 miles by 8 miles (which is half the area of a rectangle 20 miles by 12 miles). The applicant selected a rectangle 14 miles by 9 miles (which is half the area of a rectangle 18 miles by 14 miles).

So the area in question was 126 square miles.

284.
The number of distinguishable dodecahedra is 96, subdivided thus, in respect of colour distribution:

Faces 12,0	2
11,1	2
10,2	6
9,3	10
8,4	24
7,5	28
6,6	24
Total	96

285.
The original scores of 6 points to each finalist must have come from a first, second and third placing each. When the three dishonest singers reversed their order of marking, the 3 points and 1 point scored by the honest singer were reversed, but his total remained at 6. The other three finalists, however, when the marks were reversed, gained 2, lost 2, or stayed the same, depending on whether they scored 1, 2 or 3 from the honest singer. So the final scores were 8, 6, 6 and 4, and the honest singer was tied second.

286.
If the first two notes are mmmmmm-mmmmmm, then it will settle down and play mmmmmm for ever. If the first two notes are anything else, then it soon settles into this rather over-simple tune:
ping-boing-ping-boing-ping-boing. . . .

287.
The phrase, 'it reads the same either way' did not mean that it was palindromic. It meant that it read the same upside down as the right way up! It was in fact 263^2 which is 69169. This was the code number.

288.
Yes, it is. Suppose the three friends have run thirty times with these results:
For the first ten days the order of finish is Timothy, Urban, Vincent.
For the next ten days it's Urban, Vincent, Timothy.
For the last ten days it's Vincent, Timothy, Urban.
Timothy finished before Urban twenty days out of thirty.
Urban finished before Vincent twenty days out of thirty.
Vincent finished before Timothy twenty days out of thirty.

289.

The last fact given means that no one married his son and daughter to the son and daughter of the same friend.

Let us call the five friends by their initials.

'Daughter-in-law of the father of A's son-in-law' means A's daughter. 'Son-in-law of the father of C's daughter-in-law' means C's son. Then A's daughter is the sister-in-law of B's son, which can only mean that her brother (A's son) married B's daughter. Similarly, C married his daughter to D's son.

Who is the husband of D's daughter? He cannot be C's or A's son. Let us suppose he is B's son. Then C's daughter's mother-in-law is Mrs D, while A's son's mother-in-law is Mrs B. So D's daughter can't have married B's son.

It follows that D's daughter married E's son. D's daughter and B's son have a common mother-in-law: Mrs E.

Eugene's daughter is married to Bernard's son.

290.

At the start, one inch of the yellow pencil gets smeared with wet paint. As the blue pencil is moved downward, a second inch of the blue pencil's length is smeared. After the next upward movement the second inch of the blue pencil smears a second inch of the yellow pencil.

Each pair of down-up moves of the blue pencil smears one more inch of each pencil. Five pairs of moves will smear five inches. This, together with the initial inch, makes 6 inches for each pencil.

(Looking at his boots, Leonid Mikhailovich noticed that their entire lengths were muddied where they usually rub each other while he walks.

'How puzzling,' he thought. 'I didn't walk in any deep mud, yet my boots are muddied up to the knees.'

Now you understand the origin of the puzzle.)

291.

He noticed that $^7/_{12} = 1/_3 + 1/_4$, so he cut 4 sheets into 12 thirds, and 3 sheets into 12 fourths. Each worker got one third and one fourth, or $^7/_{12}$.

For the other distributions, he used:

$$^5/_6 = 1/_2 + 1/_3$$
$$^{13}/_{12} = 1/_3 + 3/_4$$
$$^{13}/_{36} = 1/_4 + 1/_9$$
$$^{26}/_{21} = 2/_3 + 4/_7, \text{ and so on.}$$

292.

They poured the shot into the jug and then poured in water, which filled all the spaces between the pellets. Now the water volume plus the shot volume equalled the jar's volume.

Removing the shot from the jar, they measured the volume of water remaining, and subtracted it from the volume of the jar.

293.
They will always reach the destination simultaneously, no matter where the bicycle is left behind for the last time.

294.
If you place the point of a compass at the centre of a black square on a chessboard with 2-inch squares, and extend the arms of the compass a distance equal to the square root of 10 inches, the pencil will trace the largest possible circle that touches only black squares.

295.
Several procedures have been devised by which n persons can divide a cake in n pieces so that each is satisfied he has at least 1/n of the cake. The following system has the merit of leaving no excess bits of cake.

Suppose there are five persons: A, B, C, D, E. A cuts off what he regards as ⅕ of the cake and what he is content to keep as his share. B now has the privilege, if he thinks A's slice is more than ⅕, of reducing it to what he thinks is ⅕ by cutting off a portion. Of course if he thinks it is ⅕ or less, he does not touch it. C, D and E in turn now have the same privilege. The last person to touch the slice keeps it as his share. Anyone who thinks that this person got less than ⅕ is naturally pleased because it means, in his eyes, that more than ⅘ remains. The remainder of the cake, including any cut-off pieces, is now divided among the remaining four persons in the same manner, then among three. The final division is made by one person cutting and the other choosing. The procedure is clearly applicable to any number of persons.

296.
The answer is that A's chances of being pardoned are ⅓, and that C's chances are ⅔.

Regardless of who is pardoned, the governor can give A the name of a man, other than A, who will die. The governor's statement therefore has no influence on A's survival chances; they continue to be ⅓.

What about prisoner C? Since either A or C must die, their respective probabilities for survival must add up to 1. A's chances to live are ⅓; therefore C's chances must be ⅔. This can be confirmed by considering the four possible elements in our sample space, and their respective initial probabilities:
1. C is pardoned, governor names B (probability ⅓)
2. B is pardoned, governor names C (probability ⅓)
3. A is pardoned, governor names B (probability ⅙)

4. A is pardoned, governor names C (probability $\frac{1}{6}$)

In cases 3 and 4, A lives, making his survival chances $\frac{1}{3}$. Only cases 1 and 3 apply when it becomes known that B will die. The chances that it is case 1 are $\frac{1}{3}$, or twice the chances ($\frac{1}{6}$) that it is case 3, so C's survival chances are two to one, or $\frac{2}{3}$.

297.

At nobody. Fire your pistol in the air, and you will have the best chance of all three of the truellists. Certainly you don't want to shoot at Black. If you are unlucky enough to hit him, Blue will polish you off on the next shot. Suppose you aim at Blue and hit him. Then Black will have first shot against you and his overall probability of winning the duel will be $\frac{6}{7}$, yours $\frac{1}{7}$. Not too good. (You are invited to confirm Black's winning probability of $\frac{6}{7}$ by summing the infinite geometric series: $\frac{2}{3}$ + $(\frac{1}{3})(\frac{2}{3})(\frac{2}{3})$ + $(\frac{1}{3})(\frac{2}{3})(\frac{1}{3})(\frac{2}{3})(\frac{2}{3})$ . . .) But if you deliberately miss, you will have the first shot against either Black or Blue on the next round. With probability $\frac{2}{3}$, Black will hit Blue, and you will have an overall winning probability of $\frac{3}{7}$. With $\frac{1}{3}$ probability, Black will miss Blue, in which case Blue will dispose of his stronger opponent, Black, and your overall chance against Blue will be $\frac{1}{3}$.

Thus by shooting in the air, your probability of winning the truel is $\frac{25}{63}$ (about 40%). Black's probability is $\frac{8}{21}$ (about 38%), and poor Blue's is only $\frac{2}{9}$ (about 22%).

Is there a lesson in this which might have application to the field of international relations?

298.

Your strategy should be quite different from that best pursued in *Twenty Questions*. One way to proceed is to start with the question 'Is your number bigger than 1?' If you get a 'yes' response, your next question will be 'Is it bigger than 2?' and so on up the line. In this manner, the first 'no' answer you receive will pinpoint your opponent's number, which you will promptly guess the next time you assume the role of questioner.

The only way your opponent can win, therefore, is to guess your number on his first round of questions. His chance of doing so is 1 out of 100, so your advantage in this game, as first questioner is 99 to 1. As the size of the range of numbers increases, the first player's advantage increases correspondingly.

299.

Let P be the probability of winning for the first player who spins. In one out of six cases, he loses immediately. In the other five, the other player will have the same probability P of winning. Thus $P = \frac{5}{6}(1-P)$ and $P = \frac{5}{11}$. Now let N be the number of chambers remaining, assuming neither player has yet exercised the spin option. The chance of winning is not better than $(N-1)(1-P)/N$ if no spin is made, and this chance is always less than $\frac{5}{11}$ except when $N = 6$, in which case it is equal to $\frac{5}{11}$. (Obviously spinning prior to the first shot does not affect the first player's odds, provided his opponent plans to spin on his turn.)

It follows that, after the first shot, it is always desirable to spin, and that prior to the first shot it apparently makes no difference! For if you elect not to spin and get a 'click', your opponent, who may not have worked out the game, is liable not to spin either, in which case (provided he also gets a 'click') you will spin prior to the third shot. By not spinning, you offer him the opportunity of foolishly lowering his odds by 4 per cent. Had you spun prior to the first shot, he would have had no opportunity of making a mistake, and would be compelled to adopt the best strategy. So your best chance is obtained by not spinning prior to the first shot, and spinning on all successive shots.

In the misère version, analysis is more difficult. Working backward, on the fifth shot, spinning gives odds of 6/11 against 1/2 without spinning. So spinning is superior at shot five. At shot four, spinning gives odds of 6/11 against $1/3 + 2/3 \times 5/11$ or 7/11 without spinning, so that no spinning is superior. At shot two, no spinning gives odds of $1/5 + (4/5 \times 5/11) = 31/55$, making no spinning the better percentage play. It follows that the first player should deny his opponent the opportunity of electing not to spin and should spin prior to his first shot, giving himself maximum odds of 6/11.

TOMORROW'S CLASSICS

300.
Apply 180-degree turns to each of the faces in the following sequence: top, bottom, right, left, front, back.

301.
Apply 180-degree turns to the following faces: front, right, back, front, right, back.

302.
Apply the following 90-degree turns: front clockwise, back anticlockwise, top clockwise, bottom anticlockwise, right clockwise, left anticlockwise, front clockwise, back anticlockwise.

303.
The answers are: 3784, 3159, 1395, 1827, 2187, 1435. The common factor is that in each multiplication, the answer consists of the same digits as the numbers being multiplied.

304.
The common factor is that each of the digits from 1 to 9 appears once and only once in the answer and the numbers being multiplied.

305.
Each of the answers, looked at upside down, spells out a word.
(a) 3704 (hole)   (b) 5710 (oils)   (c) 5733 (eels)   (d) 7105 (soil)
(e) 7714 (hill)   (f) 7734 (hell)   (g) 53751 (isles)
(h) 317537 (Leslie)

306.
(1) The car's velocity steadily increases from zero at the start to maximum at the earth's centre, and steadily decreases thereafter to zero at the other end.
(2) The car's acceleration is maximum at the start (32 feet per second per second). It decreases as it approaches the earth's centre, where it becomes zero. After that it accelerates negatively until it reaches the other end.
(3) Halfway down the tube, in a stationary car, you would weigh much less than on the earth's surface because of the gravitational pull of the earth above you.
(4) You would be in free-fall throughout the entire trip, and therefore always in a state of zero gravity.
(5) The car reaches a top speed at the earth's centre of about 17,700 mph, or almost 5 miles per second.
(6) On the moon a car falling through the moon's centre would complete the trip in about 53 minutes; on Mars, in about 49 minutes.
(7) The story is 'When the Earth screamed' by Sir Arthur Conan Doyle. It tells how Professor George Edward Challenger, the hero of Doyle's novel *The Lost World*, penetrates the earth's 'skin', causing it to howl with pain.

307.
(1) Rocket ships are in 'free fall' as soon as they leave the earth. From the time the motors are turned off to the time they are used again for altering course or braking, there is zero gravity inside a rocket ship.
(2) Cigars won't stay lit in zero gravity unless you constantly wave them about. Gases produced by the burning of tobacco must be carried upward by the buoyancy of air, in turn caused by gravity pulling air down.

(3) Birds can't fly on the moon because there is no air against which their wings can push or support them when gliding.

(4) No air, no breezes, no rippling flags on the moon.

(5) Although in daytime the lunar sky is indeed dark, there is so much reflected light from the moon's surface that stars are not visible to unaided eyes. They *can* be seen through binoculars.

(6) Even at night, stars on the moon never twinkle. Twinkling on earth is caused by movements of the atmosphere.

(7) For stars to be visible inside the arms of a crescent earth they would have to be between earth and the moon.

(8) The moon does rotate once during each revolution around the earth, but since it always keeps its same face towards the earth, the earth does not rise and set. From any given location on the earth side of the moon, the earth remains fixed in the sky.

(9) Without air a boomerang can no more operate on the moon than a bird can keep itself aloft.

(10) Twitchell couldn't have heard the boomerang strike the boulder because sound requires an atmosphere to transmit its waves to a human ear.

(11) Before the first moon landing it was widely thought that objects would be invisible in moon shadows. Actually, so much light is reflected from the irregular lunar surface that this is not the case.

(12) Although the sun does rise and set on the moon, it takes it about 28 days to return to a former position. It could not have set as rapidly as the narrative indicates.

(13) The terminator moves at about 10 miles per hour. This is slow enough for a person to keep pace with its movement.

(14) Meteors leave glowing trails only when they are burned up by friction of the earth's atmosphere. On the atmosphereless moon, meteors would not produce such trails.

(15) As in mistake 12, the sun could not have risen until some two weeks after it set.

ACKNOWLEDGMENTS

The author and publishers would like to thank the following people for permission to reproduce material which is their copyright. They have made every effort to trace copyright holders. If they have inadvertently omitted to acknowledge anyone they would be most grateful if it could be brought to their attention for correction at the first opportunity.

The *Observer* for nos 241 and 243 (crosswords by Torquemada and Ximenes).

A. F. Ritchie for no 242 (crossword by Afrit).

Michael Curl for nos 191–3, 217, 220, 221, 223, 230, 236–7, 244–6, 249–51, 309–11.

Bantam Books Inc. for nos 247–8 from *Fifty Great Crossword Puzzles 10*, © 1974.

Dover Publications, Inc. for nos 282–4 from *My Best Puzzles in Mathematics* (© 1961) by Hubert Phillips; and for nos 285–7 from *Recreations in Logic* (© 1979) by D. G. Wells.

Charles Scribner's Sons and George Allen & Unwin Ltd for nos 288 and 290 from *100 Geometric Games* (1976) and *100 Logic Games* (1977) by Pierre Berloquin, © 1973 Libraire Generale Francaise.

Charles Scribner's Sons for nos 291–4 from *The Moscow Puzzles* by Boris Kordemsky, © 1971, 1972.

Martin Gardner for nos 295–7 from *More Mathematical Puzzles and Diversions*, published by Simon and Schuster Inc., © 1961.

William Heinemann Ltd for nos 298–300 from *Your Move* (Kaye and Ward, © 1973) by David Silverman.

Penguin Books Ltd and Clarkson N. Potter Inc., for puzzles 307–8 from *Science Fiction Puzzle Tales* by Martin Gardner, © 1981.

St Louis Post for no 238.

INDEX

(the numbers refer to the pages on which the puzzles may be found)